Published by Bassline Publishing
www.basslinepublishing.com

All design and layout by Music Book Production Services
www.musicbookproductionservices.com

Every effort has been made to fulfill requirements with regard to reproducing copyright material.
The publisher will be glad to rectify any omissions at the earliest opportunity

All music transcribed and engraved by Stuart Clayton.

ISBN 13: 978-0-9557981-9-1

Notation Legend

The Stave: most music written for the bass guitar uses the bass clef. The example to the right shows the placement of the notes on the stave.

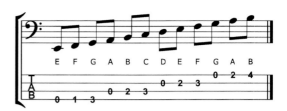

Tablature: this is a graphical representation of the music. Each horizontal line corresponds with a string on the bass guitar, with the lowest line representing the lowest string. The numbers represent the frets to be played. Numbers stacked vertically indicate notes that are played together. Where basses with five or six strings are required, the tablature stave will have five or six lines as necessary.

Notes shown in brackets indicated that a note has been tied over from a previous bar.

Repeats: the double line and double dot barlines indicate that the music between these barlines should be repeated. If the music is to be repeated more than once, a written indication will be given i.e. 'play 3x'.

1st & 2nd Time Endings: these are used for sections that are repeated, but which have different endings. The first ending is used the first time, the second is used on the repeat. The first ending is ignored on the repeat, only the second is used.

Slap: the note is slapped with the thumb.

Pop: the note is popped with either the first or second finger.

Thumb Upstroke: note is played with an upstroke of the thumb, usually following a slap

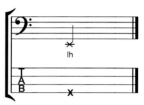

Left Hand: note is played by hammering on with the left hand.

Harmonic: note is played as a harmonic by lighting touching the string above the fret indicated.

Artificial Harmonic: fret the lower note and tap the string over the fret shown in brackets.

Trill: alternate between the notes indicated by repeatedly hammering-on and pulling-off.

Vibrato: the pitch of the note is altered by repeatedly bending and releasing the string.

Hammer-On: only the first note is struck. The second is sounded by fretting it with another finger.

Pull-Off: Only the first note is struck. Lift the fretting finger to sound the second fretted note.

Slide: play the first note, then slide the finger to the second.

Right Hand Tap: note is tapped with a finger of the right hand. If necessary, finger will be specified.

Left Hand Tap: note is tapped with a finger of the left hand. If necessary, finger will be specified.

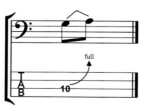

Bend: note is bent upwards to the interval indicated. ½ = semitone, full = tone.

Bend and Release: note is bent up to the interval indicated then released to the original note.

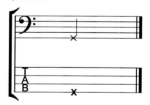

Ghost Note: note is a pitchless 'dead' note used as a rhythmic device.

Accent: note is accentuated, or played louder.

Staccato: note is played staccato - short.

Tenuto: note is held for its full length.

p   *piano* - played very softly
mp   *mezzo-piano* - played moderately quietly
f   *forte* - played loud/strong
mf   *mezzo forte* - played moderately loud/strong

D.C al Coda: Return to the beginning of the song and play until the bar marked Coda. Then jump to the section marked Coda.
D.S al Coda: Return to the sign, then play until the bar marked Coda. Then jump to the Coda.
D.C (or D.S) al Fine: Return to the point specified, then play until the Fine marking. Stop at this point.

Contents

Stuart Zender Biography — 4

Stuart Zender Gear Analysis — 5

When You Gonna Learn — 6

Too Young To Die — 13

Hooked Up — 23

If I Like It, I Do It — 32

Music Of The Mind — 43

Emergency On Planet Earth — 57

Whatever It Is, I Just Can't Stop — 65

Blow Your Mind — 75

Just Another Story — 86

Stillness In Time — 102

Light Years — 114

Manifest Destiny — 122

The Kids — 133

Mr. Moon — 146

Scam — 157

Space Cowboy — 170

Stuart Zender: Biography

Through his work with Jamiroquai in the early nineties, Stuart Zender cultivated an enviable reputation as one of UK's most influential bass players. His infectious, funk-driven bass work was undoubtedly a key part of the band's sound and has been much missed since his departure at the peak of their success in 1998. Since then he has lent his low-end talents to a range of other artists including Lauryn Hill, Omar, Stevie Wonder and Incognito. Now working as both a session bassist and a producer, he remains as popular as ever with aspiring funk bassists all over the world.

Stuart Zender was born on March 18th 1974 in Sheffield, South Yorkshire, but moved to the United States with his family at the age of seven. He grew up in Norristown, Pennsylvania, just outside of Philadelphia, a city with a notable musical heritage and the birthplace of a great deal of funk and soul music. This environment was a huge influence on Stuart as a young boy, as was being part of a musical family: his father was a pianist and his uncle a flamenco guitarist.

Stuart and his family returned to the UK when he was fifteen and he found work as a lighting engineer with the circus troupe Archaos. Although he had begun his musical life playing the drums, he also began playing bass in various bands including Fabulous, a punk band formed by NME journalist Simon Spence and photographer Martyn Goodacre. Stuart's early influences on the bass included bands such as Ozric Tentacles, Red Hot Chili Peppers and Weather Report. The latter group were an important influence on him as a teenager, so much so that he studied and learnt the entirety of their iconic *Black Market* album in just two weeks.

Stuart's break came in early 1993 after meeting singer Jay Kay through Archaos drummer Nick Van Gelder. After a few years of fronting his own group Natural Energy, Jay had auditioned as the vocalist for the Brand New Heavies. Although unsuccessful, he had become enamoured with the acid jazz/rare groove sound and had subsequently recorded the single 'When You Gonna Learn' with musicians from the Acid Jazz label. The song caught the attention of several of the major labels and Jay found himself the subject of a record label bidding

war. Eventually signed to Sony, Jay recruited Stuart and Nick to join him and keyboard player Toby Smith in his new group, Jamiroquai. The name of the band was a portmanteau of 'jam session' and 'Iroquai', the name of a Native American tribe. Augmented with a two-piece horn section, a DJ and the didgeridoo talents of Wallis Buchanan, the band recorded the *Emergency On Planet Earth* album when Stuart was just nineteen.

The first single from the album, 'Too Young to Die' was released in March 1993 and fared well in the UK charts, peaking at number 10. The band's debut album, *Emergency on Planet Earth* was even more successful, hitting the top of the UK charts upon its release in August 1993. The impact this album had on bass players upon its release was immense: Zender's funk-fuelled lines on tracks such as 'Hooked Up', 'If I Like It, I Do It', 'Music of the Mind' and 'Whatever It Is, I Just Can't Stop' were undeniably infectious, bringing to mind all of his main influences – Jaco Pastorius, Flea, Mark King, Larry Graham and Paul Jackson. Unsurprisingly, the album was voted one of the 50 best bass albums of all time (along with the two other Jamiroquai albums that Stuart played on) by the readers of *Bassist* magazine in 2000.

The bands second album, *The Return of the Space Cowboy* was released in 1995 and saw the band developing further both as performers and writers. By this point, Stuart was also developing quickly as a bassist and had expanded his tonal palette to include the use of bass effects pedals. Tracks such as 'Just Another Story' and 'The Kids' are notable examples of this and feature his use of the Boss ME-8B and Mutron pedals, both of which would soon become a regular part of the Zender sound. The album was another huge success for the band and yielded several hit singles including 'Half the Man', 'Stillness in Time' and 'Space Cowboy', which was particularly successful in the U.S., reaching #1 on the Dance Chart.

Jamiroquai's third album *Travelling Without Moving* was released just a year later in 1996 and quickly brought the band to worldwide attention. Hit singles such as 'Virtual Insanity', 'Cosmic Girl' and 'Alright' were huge hits both in the UK and internationally, and all featured killer lines from Stuart. Further bass highlights could be found in the Latin jazz workout of 'Use the Force', the gorgeous low-end throb of 'Everyday', the effects-soaked 'High Times' and the album's title track, 'Travelling Without Moving'.

Unfortunately, internal conflicts had begun to rear their heads within the band by this point and Zender made the decision to part ways with the group following an argument over writing and production credits.

After leaving Jamiroquai, Stuart began working as a session bassist, collaborating with his partner Melanie Blatt (of girl group All Saints), and playing on songs for hip-hop artists Lauryn Hill and D'Angelo. Sessions with soul singer Omar also led him to record bass on a song for legendary musician Stevie Wonder.

After a few years during which he and Melanie raised their daughter, Stuart re-emerged in 2006 playing bass for acclaimed producer Mark Ronson. Zender appeared on the songs 'Stop Me' and 'Apply Some Pressure' from the hit album *Version*, which consisted of Motown-style cover versions of popular songs. When Ronson went on tour to promote the album, Stuart was hired as the band's bassist and musical director.

Over the last decade Stuart has continued as a session musician. In 2008 he played on 'Cold Shoulder' from Adele's acclaimed album *19*, and in 2010 he was a guest on the song 'Lowdown' with funk group Incognito. He worked with Incognito again in 2016, guesting on two songs from the band's *In Search of Better Days* album: 'Love Born in Flames' and 'Echoes of Utopia'.

In addition to his recent work with Incognito, Stuart has kept busy with studio work, producing and playing on 'Everybody Needs Love' by Zak Abel and 'Love Shoes' by The Barberettes.

Stuart Zender: Gear Analysis

Stuart's first bass was an unidentified budget instrument, which he used with the various bands he worked with before joining Jamiroquai. Upon joining the band, he purchased a Warwick Streamer Stage 1 with a natural finish, which was then used for the entirety of *Emergency on Planet Earth*. He then remained a Warwick user for several years, moving to Streamer Stage II basses shortly after the recording of the band's second album. He had two very memorable models built for him, the first of which was the chrome 'Ender' bass, which had green fretboard LEDs. The second was the 'Iroquai bass', which was decorated with the pattern from a Native American blanket worn by Chief Joseph of the Iroquai tribe, from whom the band took part of their name. This bass had red fretboard LEDs. Unfortunately, both of these instruments were stolen during the nineties and Stuart has often stated that he is keen to have them back. In addition to these instruments, whilst in Jamiroquai he also owned an 8-string Warwick bass and another Stage II in white, with blue LEDs. This latter bass was restored for him by Warwick in 2015.

During recording sessions for the second Jamiroquai album *The Return of the Space Cowboy*, Stuart also used an Alembic Essence bass and a '74 Fender Jazz Bass. The Alembic bass was later stolen from his car.

Whilst working with Mark Ronson in 2008, Stuart began using a Gibson Les Paul bass strung with flatwound strings. He then reverted to Warwick in 2010, with whom he developed a striking signature instrument. The Stuart Zender Signature Bass was based on the Streamer I with a deeper cutaway for upper fret access – Stuart had actually cut a section out of the body of his original Streamer bass to make playing in the upper register easier. The body shaping is a little more extravagant and the fretboard is decorated with large, triangular fret markers, which were a nod to the triangular pattern of his old Iroquai bass. There is also a large, stylised 'SZ' motif at the twelfth fret.

Stuart also regularly uses a '63 Fender Precision bass, which he can be seen playing in the video for the Incognito track 'Love Born in Flames'.

Stuart used effects heavily during his time with Jamiroquai, most commonly an envelope filter effect. This was usually provided by Boss ME-6B and ME-8B multi-effects units – good examples of Stuart's use of these effects can be heard on 'The Kids' and 'Just Another Story', from *The Return of the Space Cowboy*. In 2017 Ashdown collaborated with Stuart on the 'Funk Face', a new pedal which features both fuzz and wah effects.

During the early part of his time with Jamiroquai, Stuart used SWR amplification, later moving to Warwick. He used the Wamp 400 head with 410-80 cabinets for several years, before switching to a Trace Elliot V-Type setup. During the 2000s he used an Ampeg rig for a while before switching to a Warwick Jonas Hellborg signature bass rig.

When You Gonna Learn

Written By: Jason Kay

'When You Gonna Learn' was the band's debut single and was originally released by Acid Jazz Records on 31st October 1992. It spent two weeks in the UK charts, peaking at #52. After Jamiroquai signed to Sony in 1993 it was re-released, but only remained in the charts for a week, peaking at #69. Despite this, it became a popular part of the band's repertoire and was frequently performed live during their early tours.

'When You Gonna Learn' was recorded before the initial Jamiroquai line-up had been established and consequently the bassline was played by Brand New Heavies bassist Andrew Levy, who had been hired to record the line for the single. The original recording of the song was considerably longer, with the album version created as an edited down version.

The song begins with a didgeridoo Intro played by Wallis Buchanan. This is followed by two bars of strings, before the band enters. In what would become a common fixture for the band, the song features an unorthodox chord progression, with many of the complex chords hinting at the band's jazz/funk leanings. Levy's bassline for the repeating four-bar Verse sections of the song is centred around a root-fifth-octave figure with a chromatic walking part connecting the Cm^9 and Fm^9 chords. A staccato octave figure, commonly found in funk and disco music is used in the fourth bar of the sequence to ascend from the B$^\flat$ back to C. The pattern for the Verse remains predominantly the same throughout, with just a few small rhythmic variations.

The Chorus is another repeating four-bar figure with an unusual chordal structure. Levy plays a pumping root-octave quaver pattern during the first bar and follows it with a more rhythmically elaborate root-octave part in the second bar. Slides, rests and ghost notes are vital to the groove here, as are the staccato markings in the first bar.

The bass is absent from the majority of the Didgeridoo Solo, entering only in the eighth bar with a descending C minor pentatonic run that is very low in the mix. As the song moves into the final Chorus section, Levy throws in a few rhythmic variations such as those found in bars 81 and 93.

Although this track was a popular part of the band's set in their early years, it is now rarely played live. Its most recent outing was in 2013, during some of the band's summer festival shows.

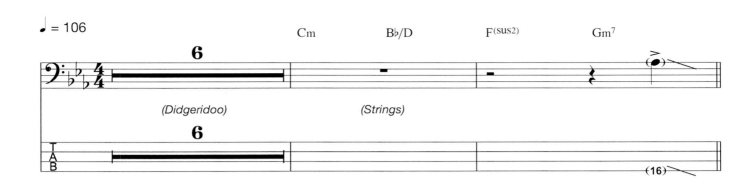

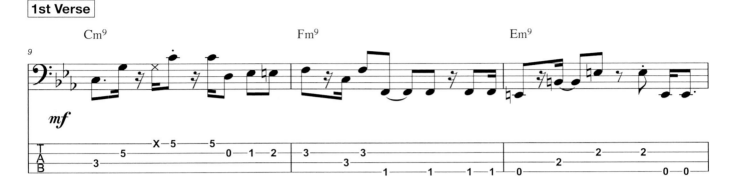

1st Verse

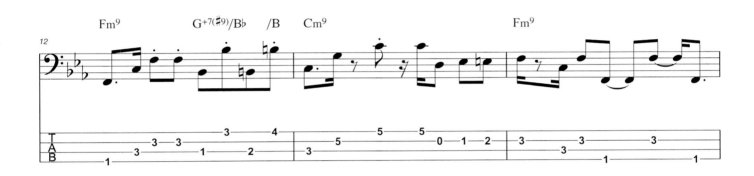

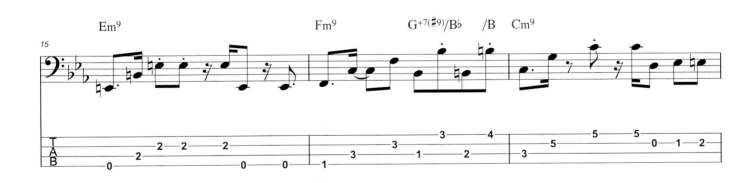

7

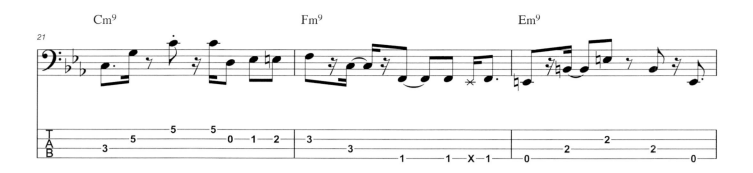

Chorus

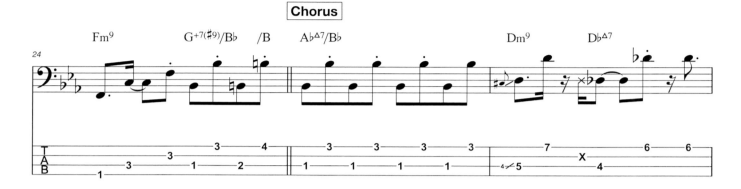

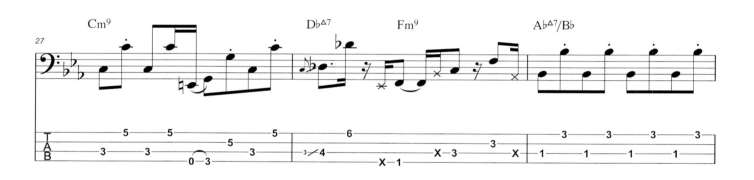

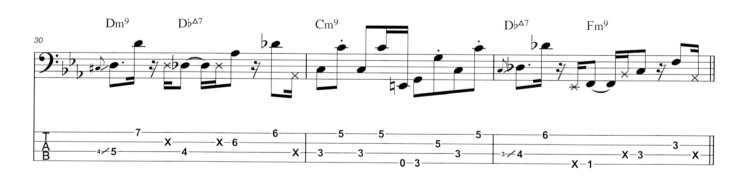

2nd Verse

8

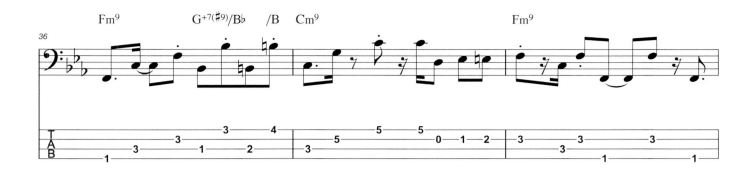

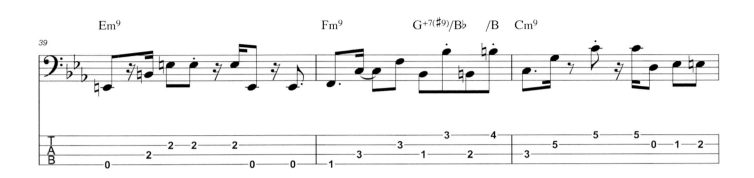

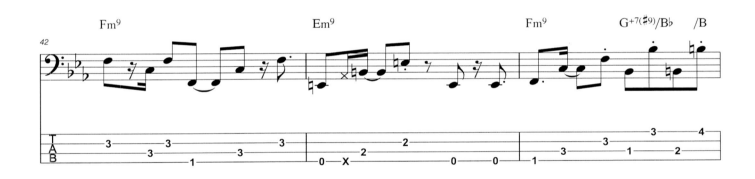

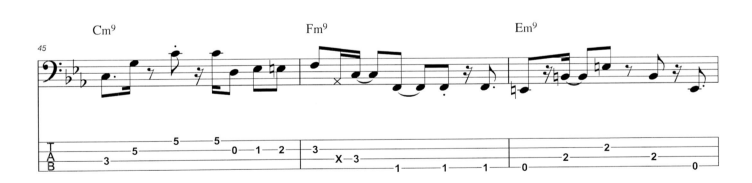

Chorus

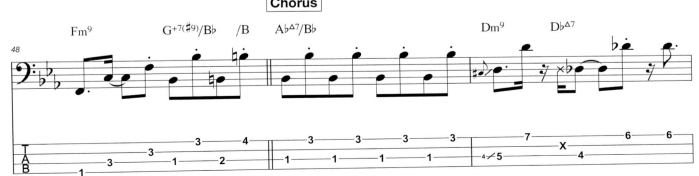

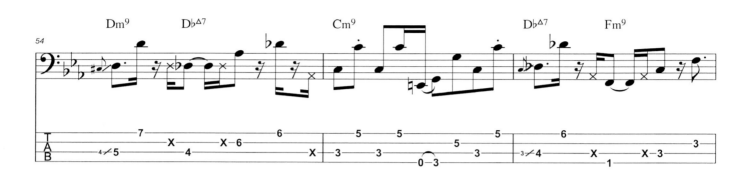

Breakdown

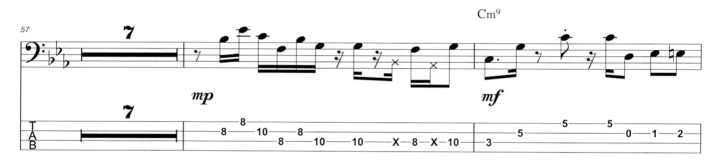

10

Outro

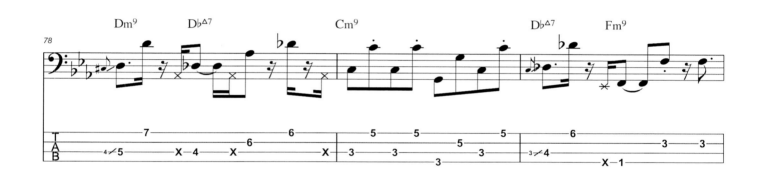

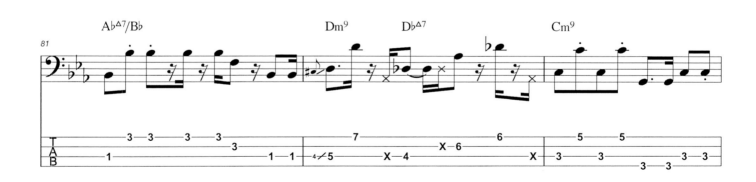

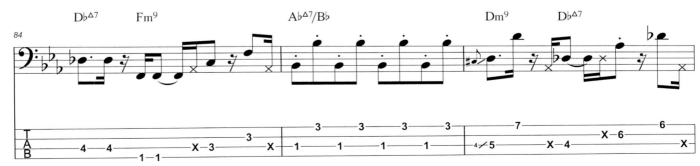

11

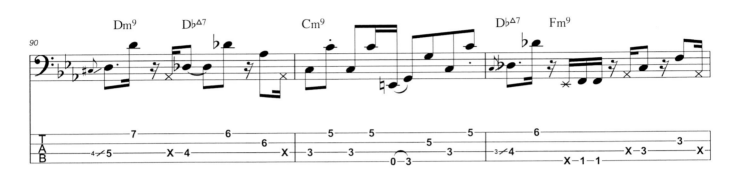

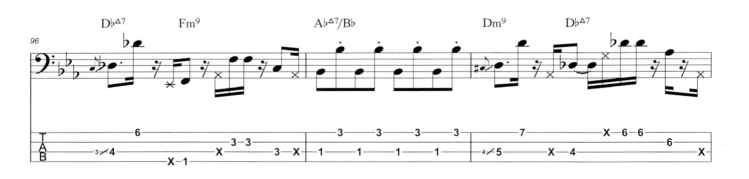

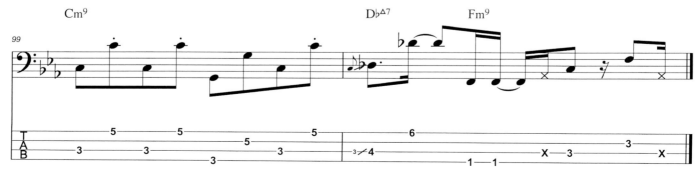

12

Fade Out

Too Young to Die

Written By: Jason Kay/Toby Smith

'Too Young to Die' was the second single from the _Emergency on Planet Earth_ album and was released on 1st March 1993. The original recorded version was over ten minutes in length and was edited down to approximately six minutes for the album (as transcribed here) and just over three minutes for the single release.

The track opens with a slow Intro featuring keys and strings - this section is played with some freedom. As the harmony builds to a climax, an ascending melodic figure - which is played in time - leads us into the main groove.

The bassline that begins in bar 6 is a repeating figure that is uses an unusual six-bar phrase length. This section is used for several different sections of the song. Stuart plays a melodic bass groove here that is arguably one of the key hooks of the track. The majority of the line is built up from chord tones with occasional chromatic passing notes (such as the $G^\flat$ in bar 7 and the B at the end of bar 9) being added to lend harmonic interest. Note the use of a simple root-fifth-octave phrase in bar 11 over the $A^{\flat\triangle9}$ and F/G chords. This is a simple line to play, but challenging in terms of getting it to feel good. Rests and articulation are crucial to the groove here, so pay attention to hammer-ons, slides, ghost notes, rests and staccato dots. Note that staccato dots do not appear in the TAB, only the notation.

The Chorus begins at bar 30 and features a completely different line based on a repeating two bar chord progression. In the first bar Stuart outlines the harmonic movement between the Cm^9 and $D^\flat m^9$ chords with simple root-fifth-octave figures but augments them with muted ghost notes to add an extra level of rhythmic interest to the line. The line in the second bar of the Chorus is again built from chord tones and is highly syncopated. Once again, the use of rests is crucial to the groove here. Stuart alternates his line in the second bar of the phrase between those found in bars 31 and 33.

The Instrumental section beginning in bar 70 features a similar line to the main verse groove, but with a couple of twists: an ascending chromatic figure at the end of the second bar of the line (bar 71) and a different turnaround in bar 75. This turnaround bar features an ascending octave figure that is slapped and popped. This section leads into a Breakdown section which is heavily syncopated and is also played with the slap technique.

This track was played frequently during the band's early years, but largely disappeared from their set-list during the late nineties and early 2000's. It was most recently played in 2017, on some shows from the _Automaton_ tour.

(Strings & Keys)

1st Verse

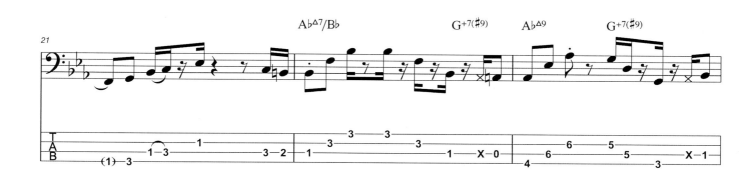

Chorus

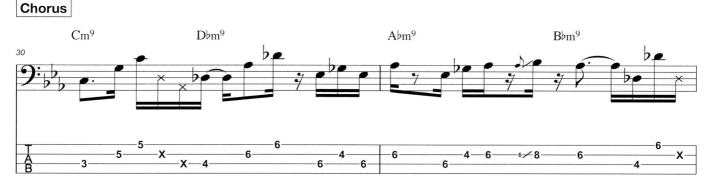

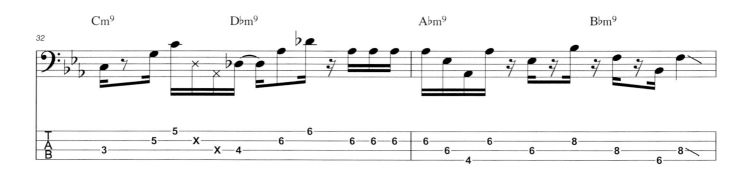

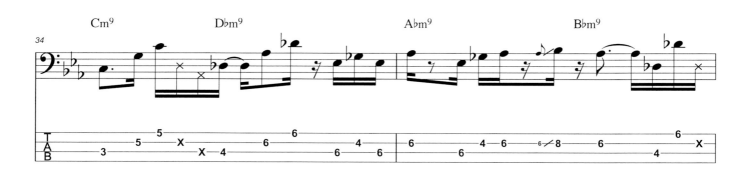

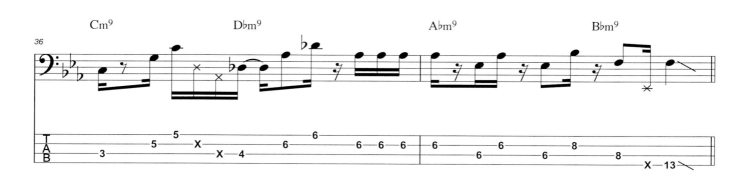

2nd Verse

16

Chorus

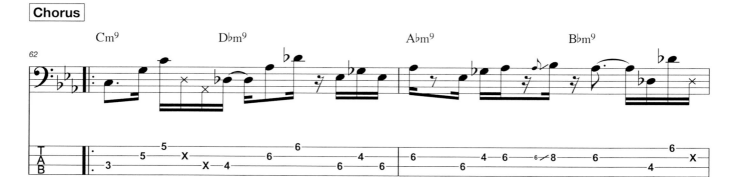

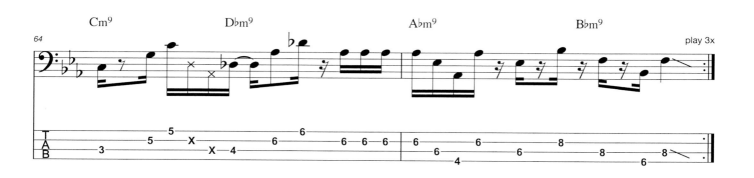

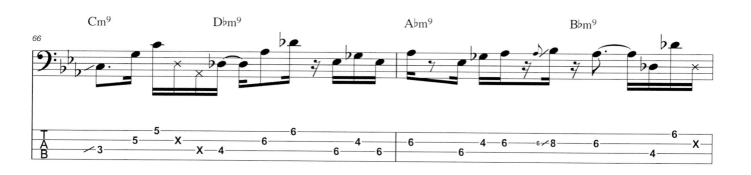

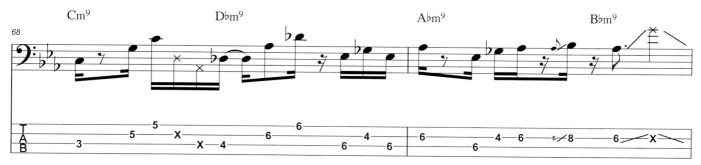

Instrumental Section

Breakdown

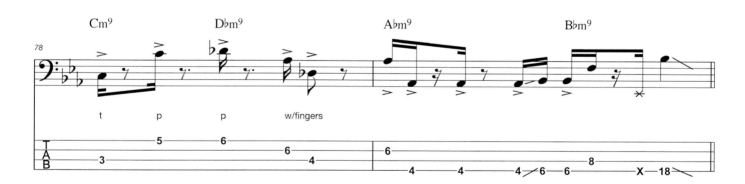

Trumpet Solo

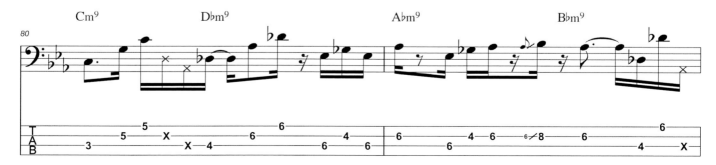

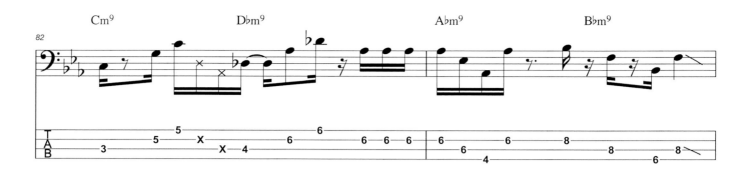

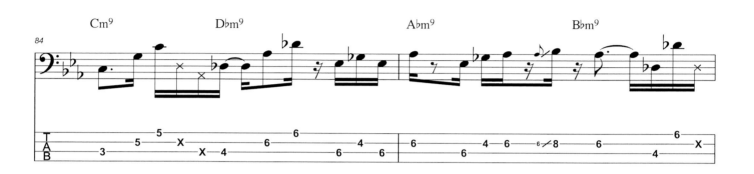

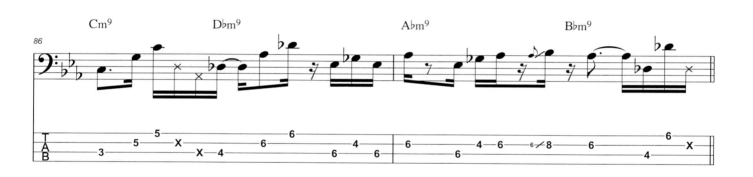

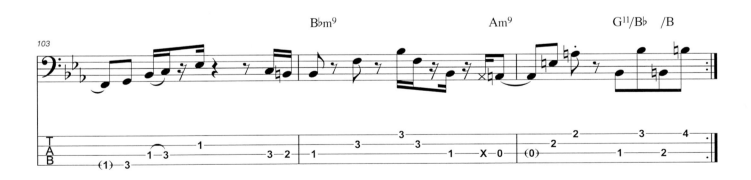

Chorus

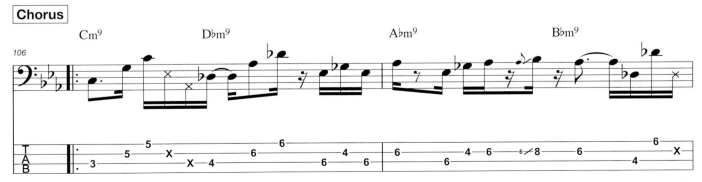

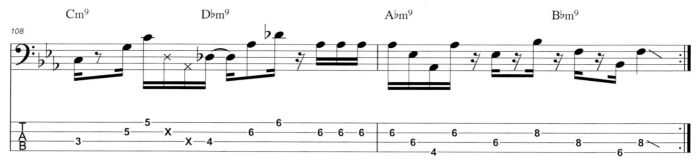

Repeat to Fade

Hooked Up

Written By: Jason Kay

'Hooked Up' is one of the funkiest tracks on the *Emergency on Planet Earth* album an(bassline from Stuart Zender.

The song opens with a Rubato (free time) keyboard riff, which is followed by eight bars of drums and percussion. Zender's bass enters at the end of bar 10 with a repeating 4-bar bass groove that features an ongoing sixteenth note anticipation of the first and third beats in each bar. This line is used for many of the parts of this track and is based on ascending chromatic lines which sometimes make it difficult to discern the overall tonality. Note that keys player Toby Smith plays some unusual chords using quartal harmony during the Verse sections (see bars 27-29 for example), further adding to the unsettled sound of the harmony.

The band switches to a new groove at letter B, and Stuart plays a sparse, heavily syncopated line that is decorated with octave-fifth drops (see bar 40) and minor pentatonic-based decorations. This section serves as a prelude to the third groove which begins at letter C and is based around a C7 tonality. Note that the bassline and melody both use the C minor pentatonic scale during these sections of the piece – although this scale includes a minor third (E♭), it is typically used against dominant chord sounds for colour. The three sections described above are used for the remainder of the track, although with some variations.

Stuart most likely recorded this track using his Warwick Streamer Stage 1 bass. As you'll hear, he used an envelope filter effect throughout, most likely suppplied by his Boss ME-6B or ME-8B multi-effects unit. This effect becomes more evident during the C and F sections, where he is playing aggressively, causing the pedal to react more obviously. When playing these sections of the song, I recommend that you play with your fretting hand closer to the end of the neck, where you can really dig in.

'Hooked Up' was occasionally played live on the band's early tours and was most recently heard in an updated version in 2010 on the *Rock Dust Light Star* tour.

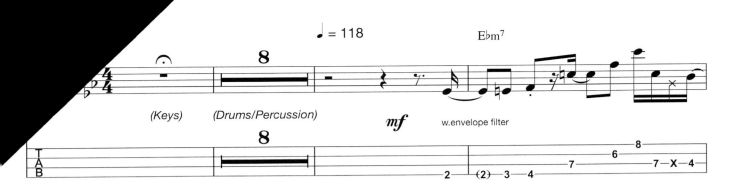

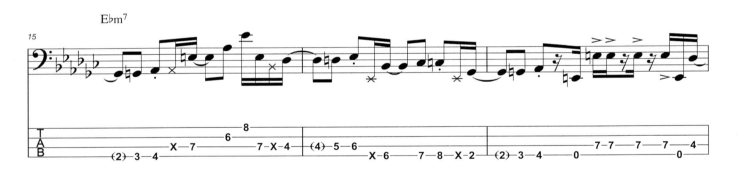

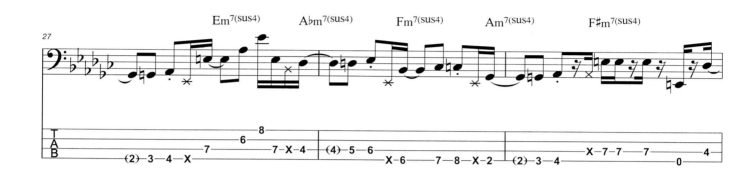

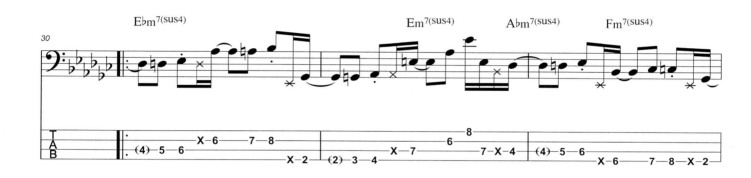

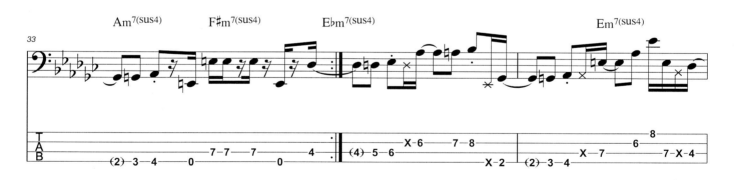

B

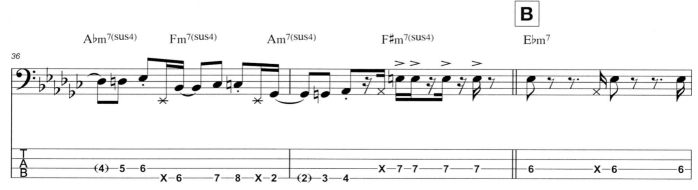

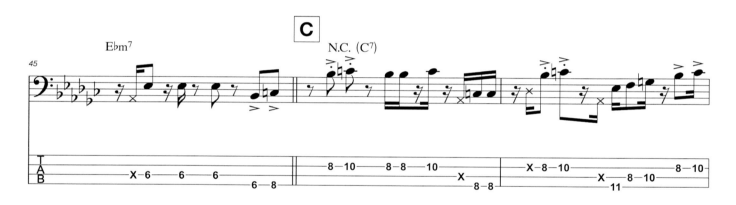

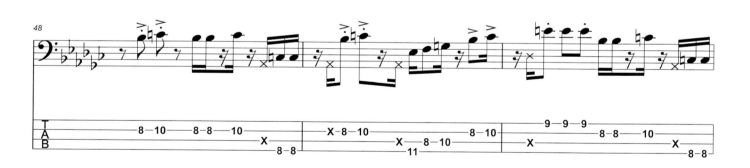

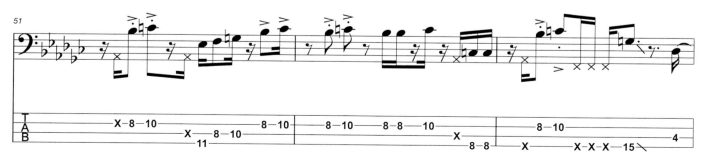

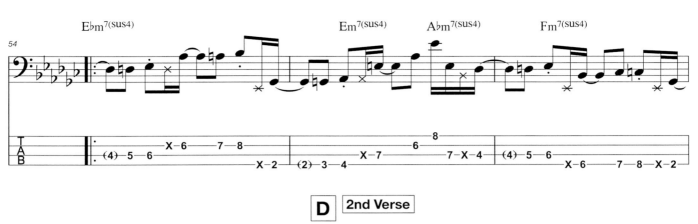

D **2nd Verse**

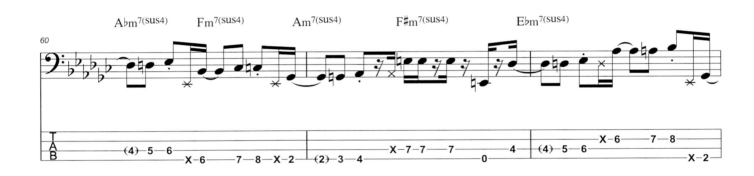

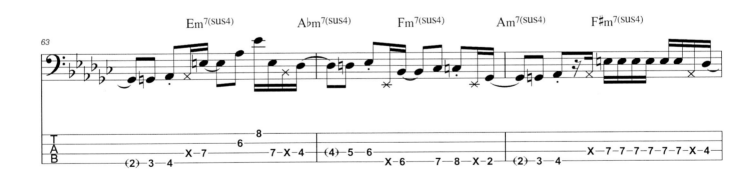

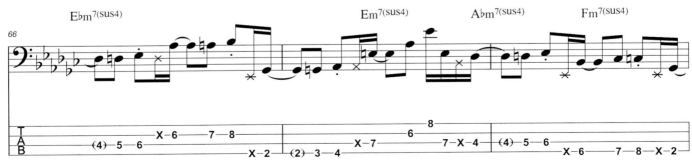

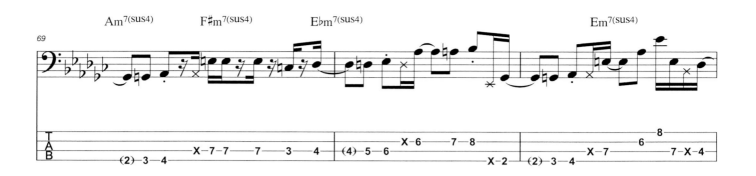

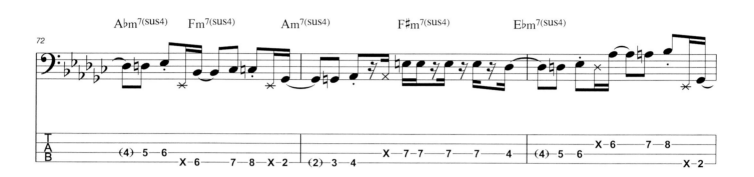

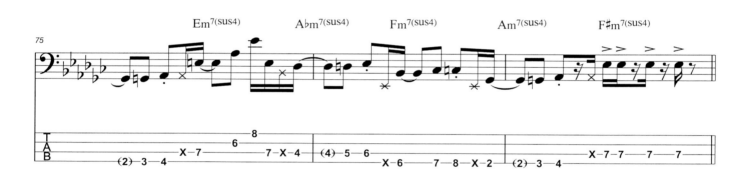

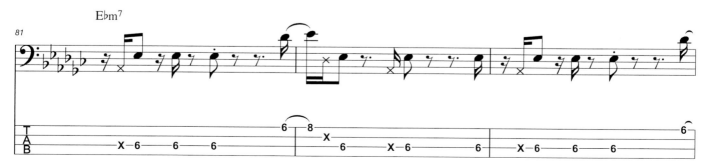

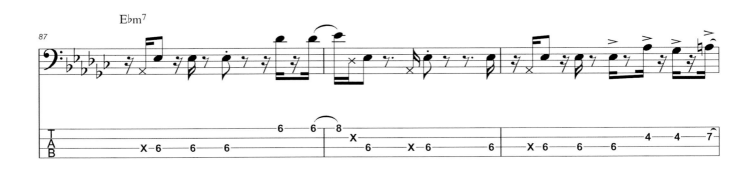

F

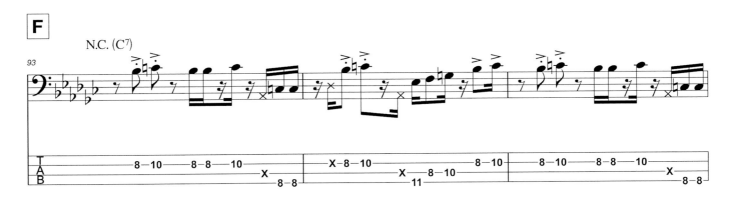

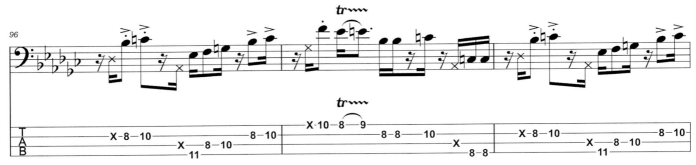

29

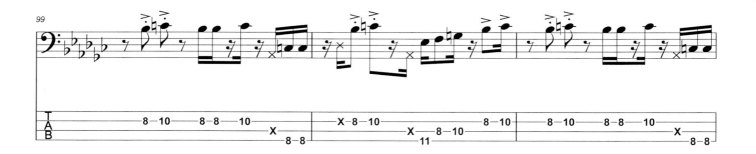

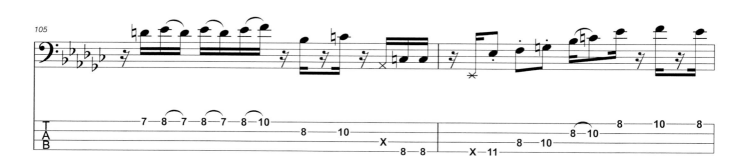

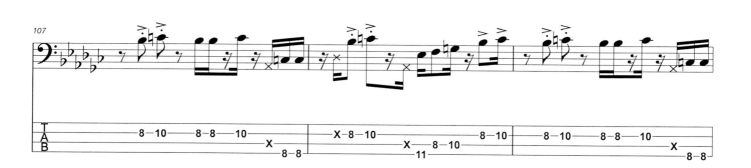

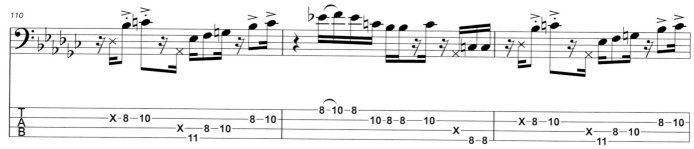

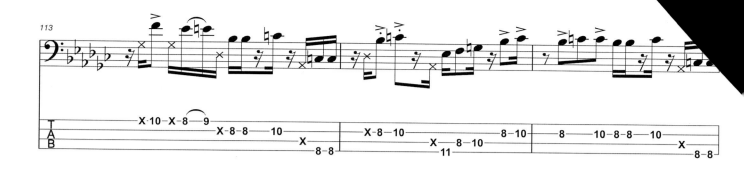

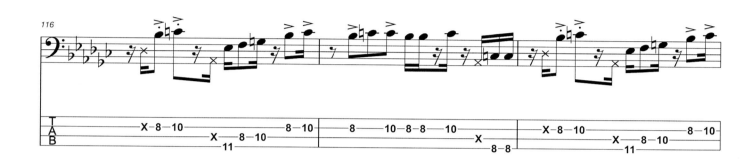

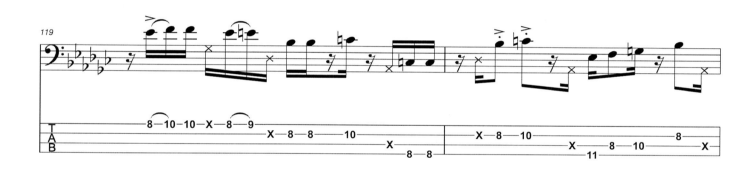

N.C.

'ke It, I Do It

ı Kay/Nick Van Gelder

'If I Like It, I Do It' is one of the best pop songs on the band's debut album and was written by singer Jason Kay and drummer Nick Van Gelder, in his only song-writing contribution with the band.

After the heavy funk of 'Hooked Up', this song feels like a welcome change of pace. Nevertheless, this track is another of the album's many bass highlights, with a superb performance from the young Stuart Zender.

The song opens with a twelve-bar Intro, the first four bars of which are based around a $D^{\triangle 7}$ tonality. Stuart opts for a simple line initially, outlining the basic chord with just root, fifth and octave, ascending then descending. There is a simple turnaround fill at the end of every second bar – note the use of the sixth (B) in this line, a subtle Motown/R&B-influence. From bar 5 onwards the chords change in each bar, allowing Stuart more scope to develop his line. He continues with the basic root, fifth and octave idea in the second bar (Em^7), then adds a little spice in the next two bars by sliding up to the ninth of each chord. Check out the cool syncopation of the $C^\sharp$ in bar 7 as well.

The first Verse begins at bar 13 and Stuart changes his part completely to suit the new chord progression. Note how he starts his line with a descending lick from F, despite the backing chord of $D^{\triangle 7}$, which contains an $F^\sharp$. This is a heavily syncopated groove, and rests and ghost notes are absolutely crucial to the feel here. The offset pitched notes in bar 15 (the third bar of the sequence) are a great touch.

Stuart's line gets busier for the Chorus section, which is based on an eight-bar chord sequence. Stuart favours a heavily syncopated blues scale in the first bar and follows this with a D Mixolydian-based line in the following bar, curiously over the Dm^7 chord. The use of the $F^\sharp$'s in this line conflict with the minor tonality of the chord (which contains an F), although there seems to be no noticeable clash, presumably because the notes go by quickly (he plays a similar part in bar 57, playing a B Mixolydian line over the Bm^7 chord). Also of note is Stuart's slick upper register fill in bar 35 as he ascends to the ninth and eleventh of the Dm^7 chord.

The three parts described above are reused throughout the song, but with the Chorus groove in particular, there are many embellishments.

As with all of the tracks on *Emergency on Planet Earth*, Stuart used his Warwick Streamer Stage 1 bass on this song.

This track was very rarely played during the band's early years, but began to occasionally creep into the set from 2006 onwards. A great version – which can be found on YouTube – was played during the band's show at the Jazz Café in London in 2006.

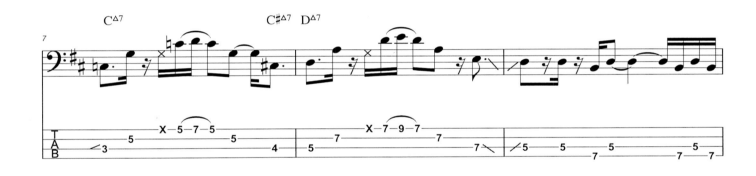

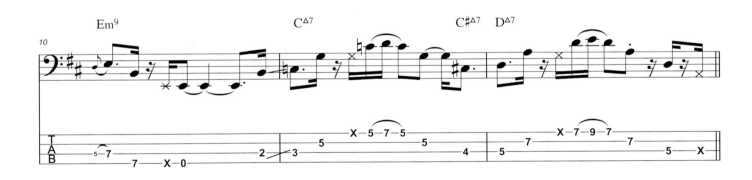

1st Verse

33

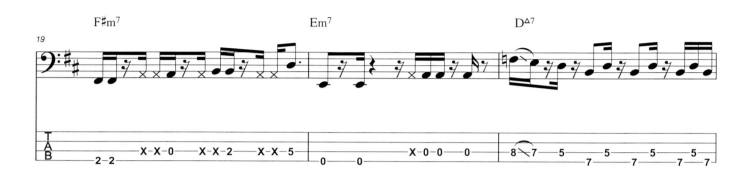

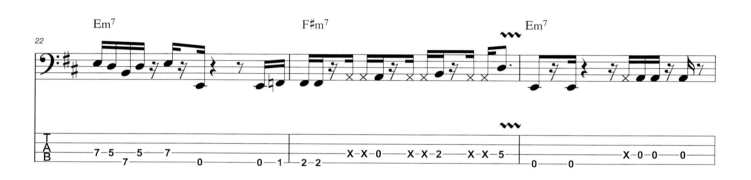

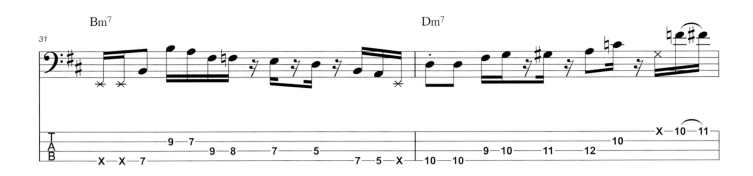

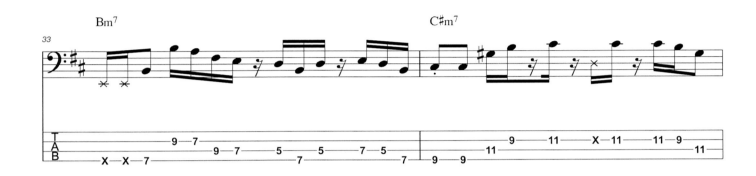

Re-Intro

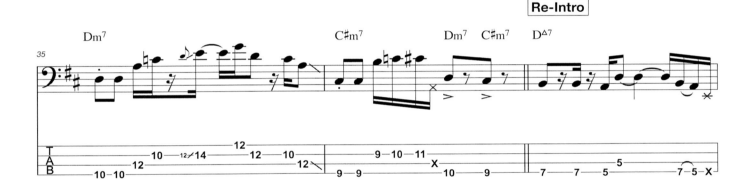

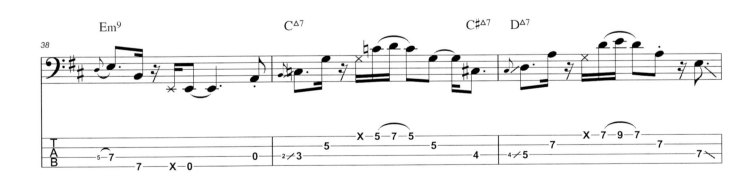

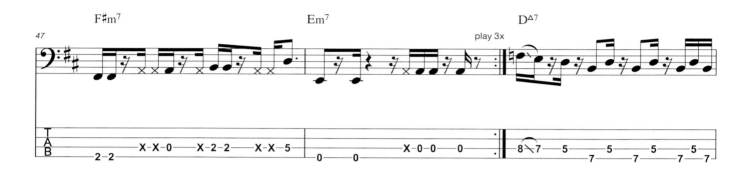

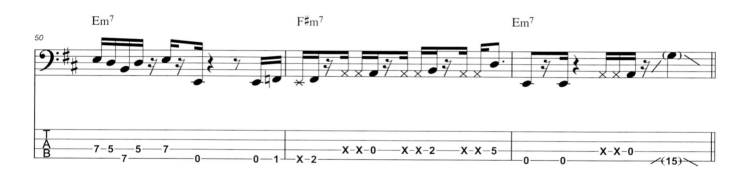

Chorus

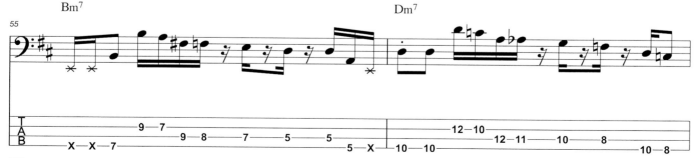

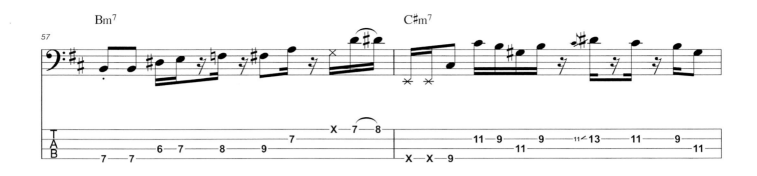

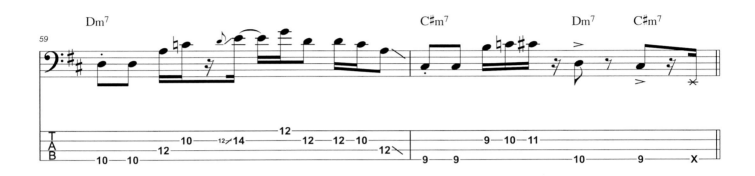

Breakdown

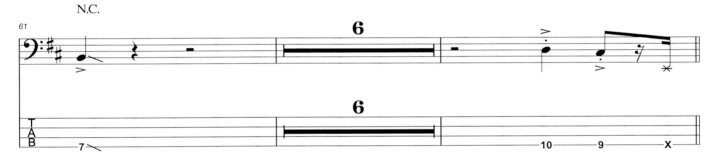

Chorus

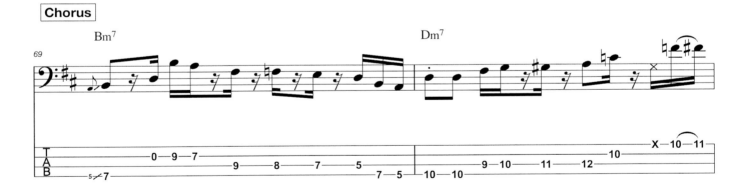

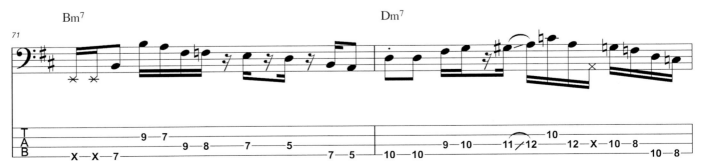

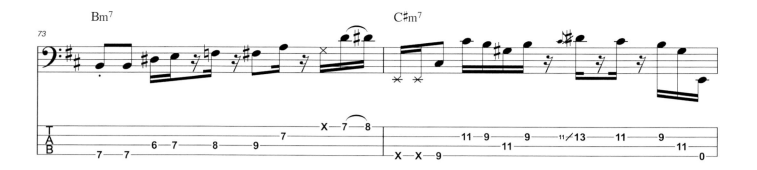

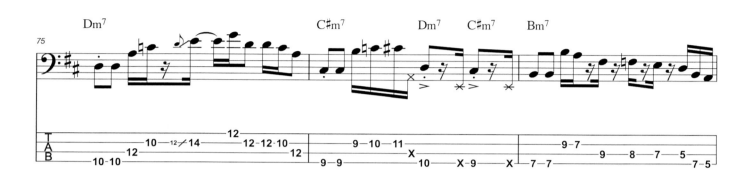

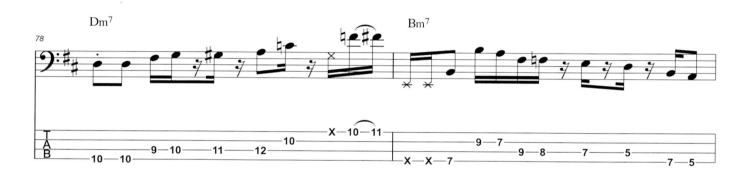

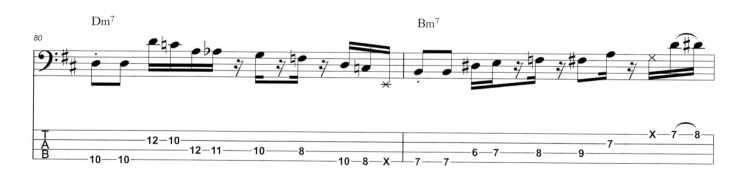

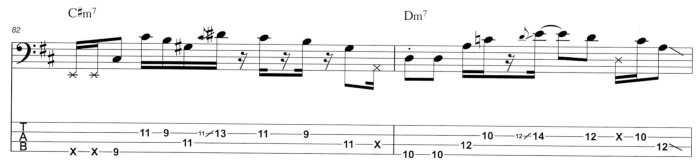

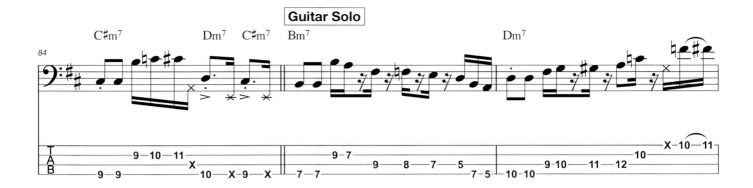

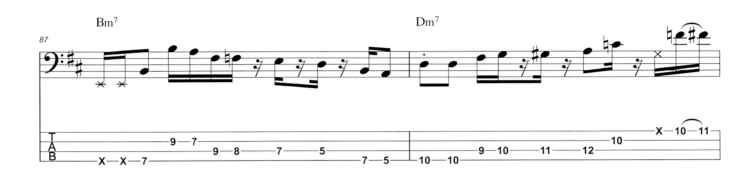

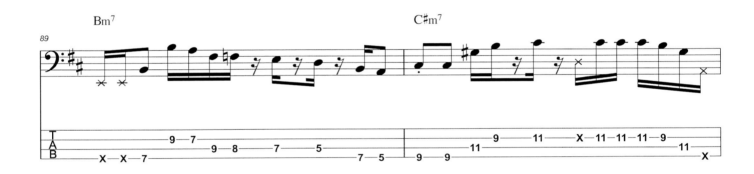

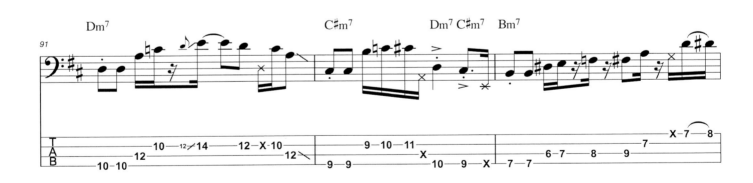

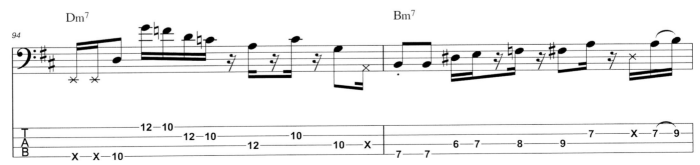

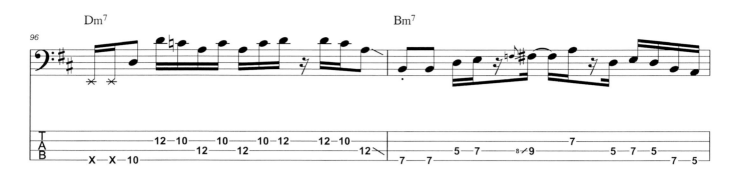

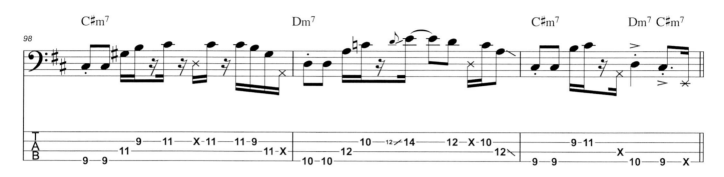

DJ Solo

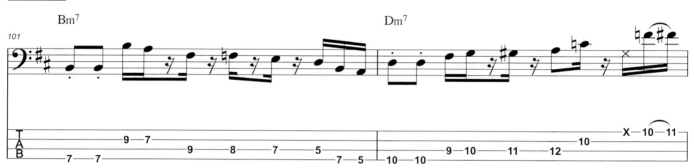

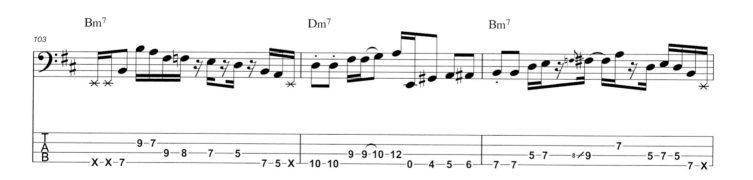

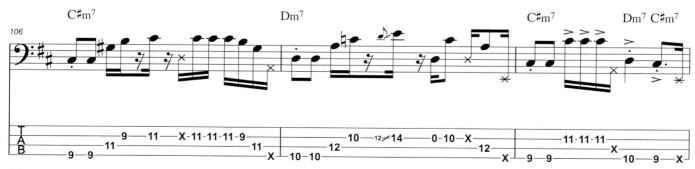

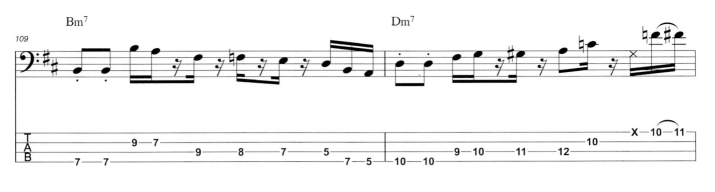

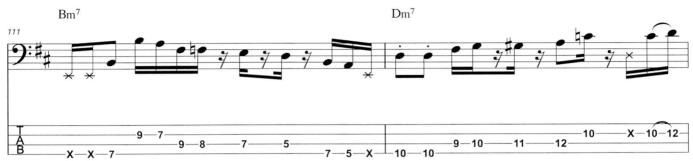

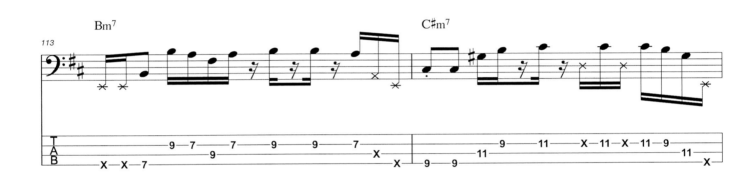

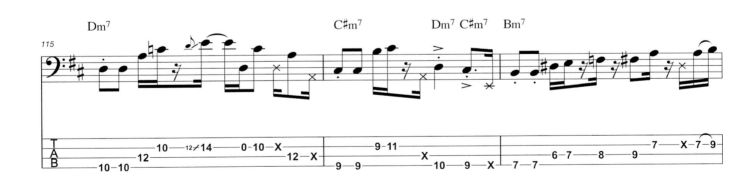

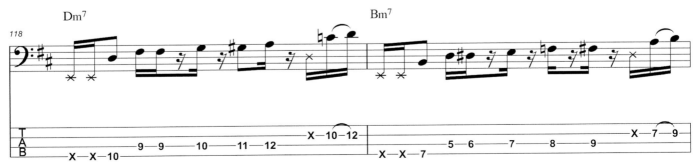

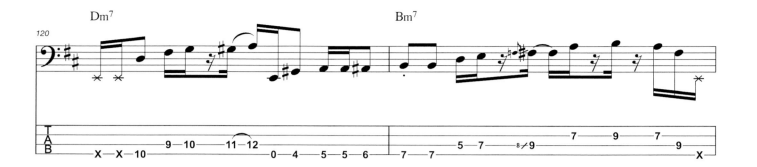

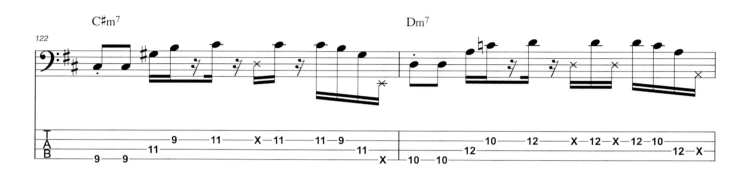

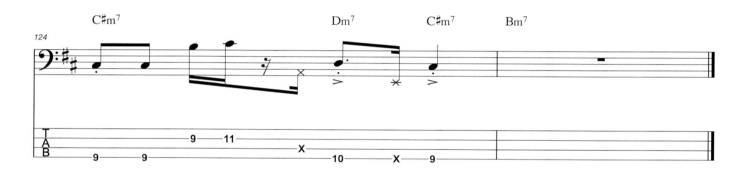

Music Of The Mind

Written By: Jason Kay/Toby Smith

'Music of the Mind' is an instrumental track from *Emergency on Planet Earth* and is undeniably one the highlights of the album, featuring some incredible bass work from the young Stuart Zender. The track actually began life as a rather different song - with a vocal part from Jason Kay - but was subsequently reworked as an instrumental. Nick Van Gelder, the band's original drummer, released an early demo version of this song onto YouTube in 2010 which is certainly worth hearing.

The main groove begins after 26 seconds of free-time keys and percussion. The song is based around an eight-bar sequence of minor-ninth chords, each played for two bars each. Stuart begins his line by outlining the tonality of the chords using a root-fifth-ninth figure. This is sometimes adapted to include the minor third of the chord, such as in bars 11 and 12. This part - which is simple but very effective - continues for several repeats of the sequence, as Zender gradually develops his line. Two bars of crotchet triplets over the Fm^9 chord (bars 65 and 66) signal a change of gear and the band takes things up a notch.

At letter B Stuart continues with the same root-fifth-ninth idea, but uses this as the basis for a much busier Latin-style groove. Again, he occasionally adds the minor third of the chord into the line to reinforce the harmony. From bar 83 onwards he begins to add more ghost notes into his bass groove which really drives the track forward. This new, busier line underpins the trumpet solo at letter C. At letter D there is an 8-bar respite from the hectic groove as the band plays a series of accents on each chord, before moving back to the busier groove for Toby Smith's piano solo, beginning at letter E. The track builds to a climax during this section, ending with another series of crotchet triplets which are used as a metric modulation to transition to the final section of the piece. This final section has a much quicker tempo, a 3-4 time signature and a new chord sequence. Stuart plays a simple walking line around the two chords, peppering his simple part with triplet fills such as those found in bars 165, 166 and 169. The track fades out on this section.

This piece was rarely heard live, even in the band's early days. It has appeared in truncated form a little more recently, during some shows in 2005 and 2013.

♩ = 138

CD Time 0.26

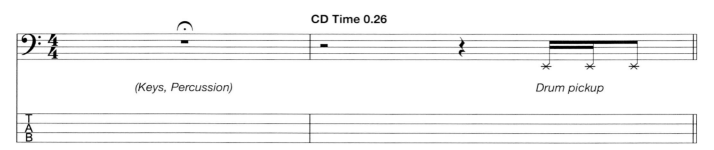

(Keys, Percussion)   Drum pickup

A

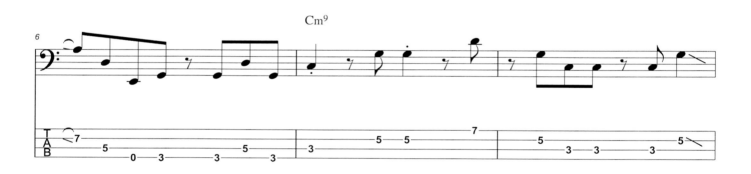

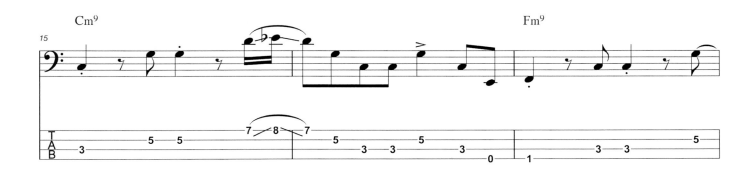

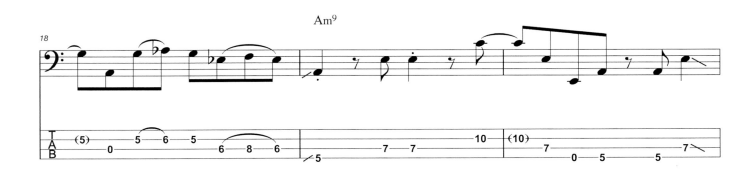

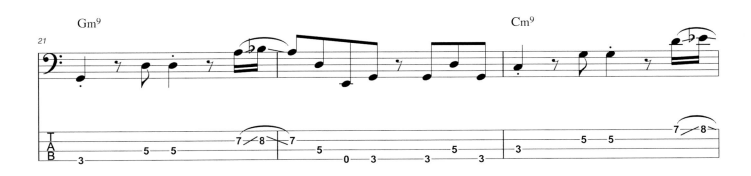

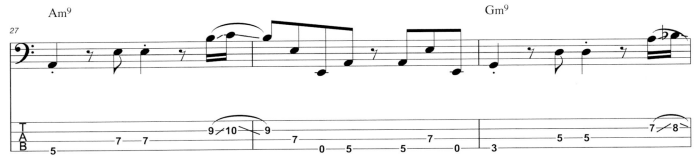

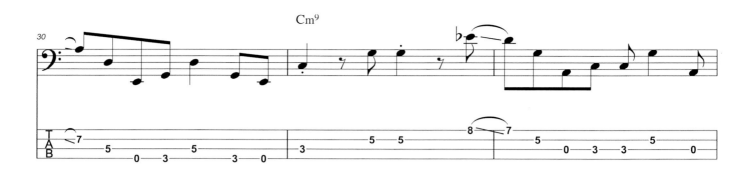

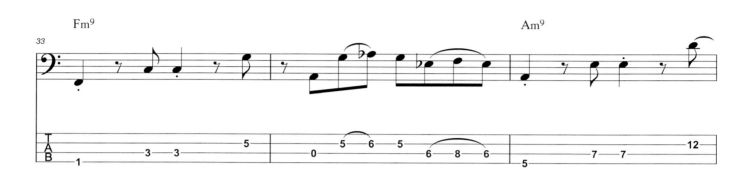

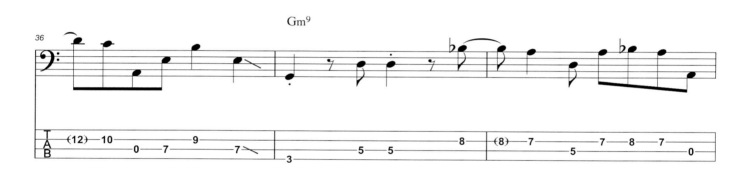

46

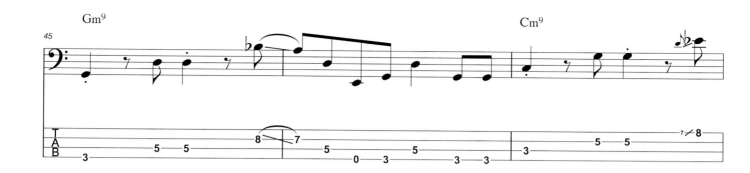

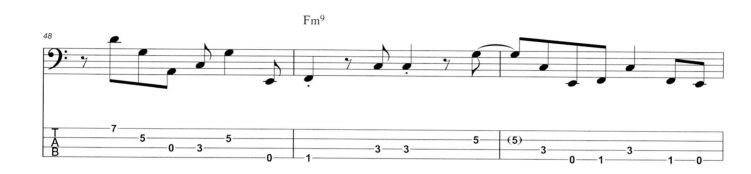

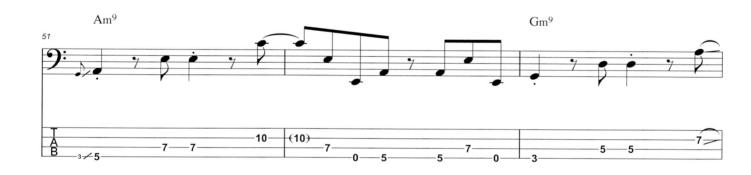

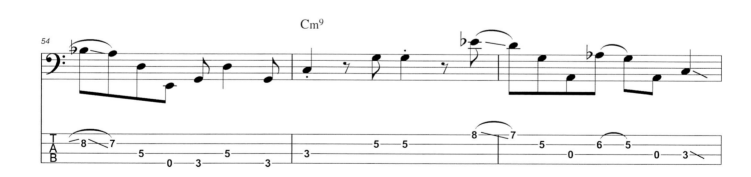

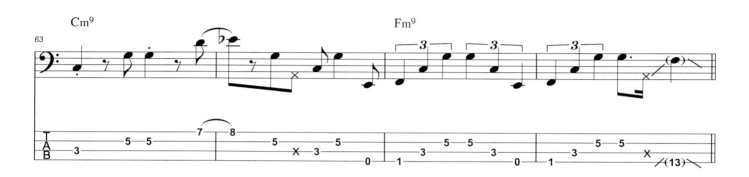

B

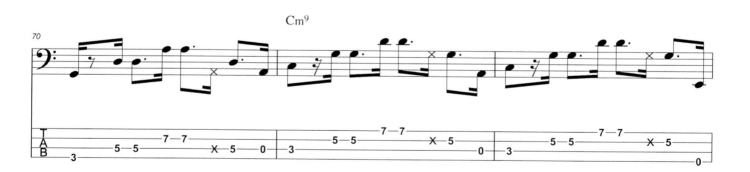

48

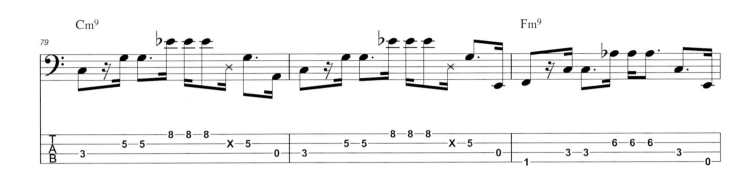

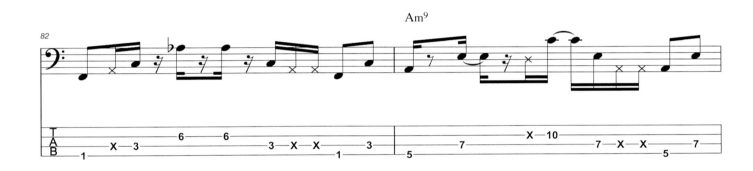

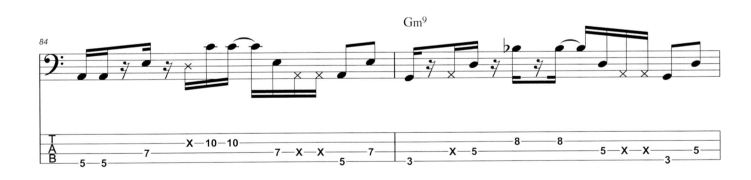

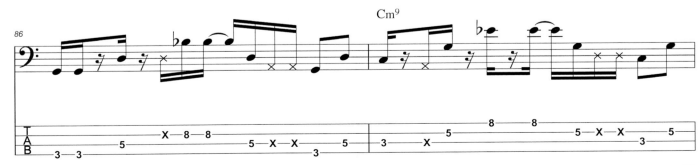

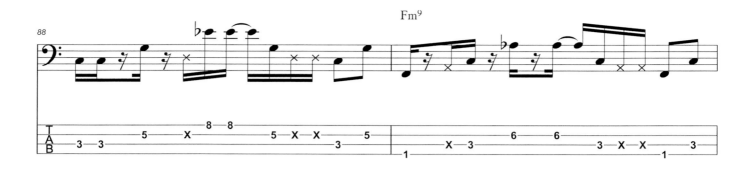

Fm⁹

C Trumpet Solo

Am⁹

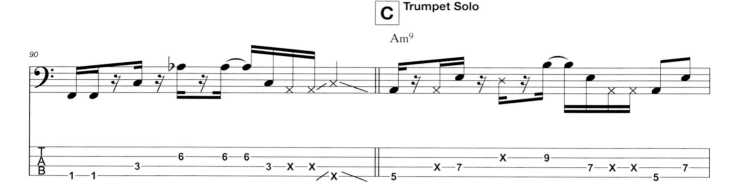

Gm⁹

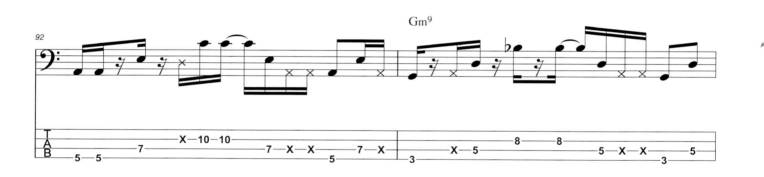

Cm⁹

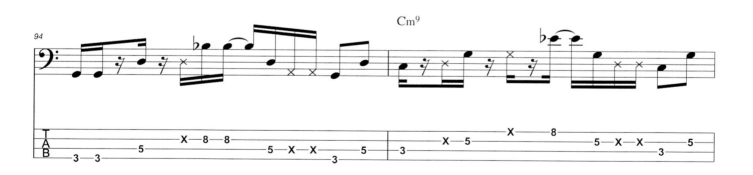

Fm⁹

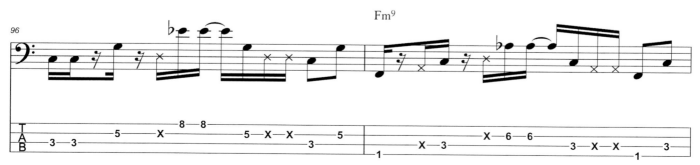

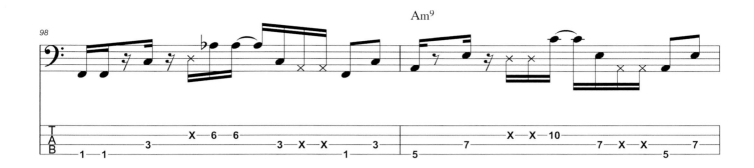

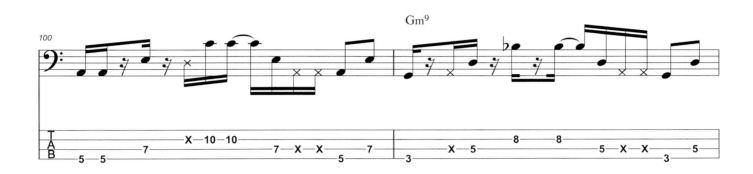

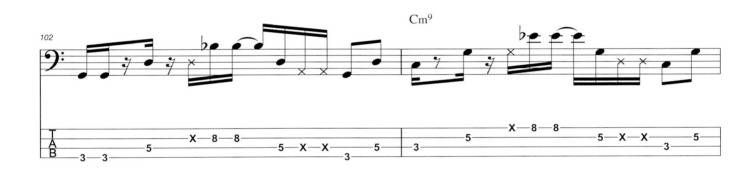

D

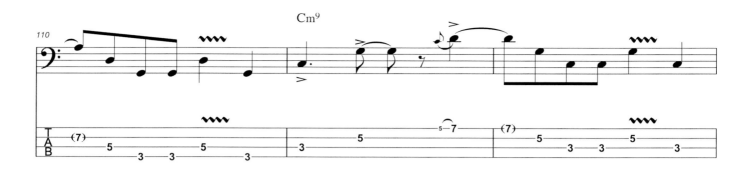

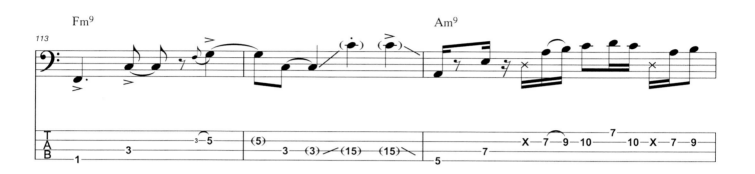

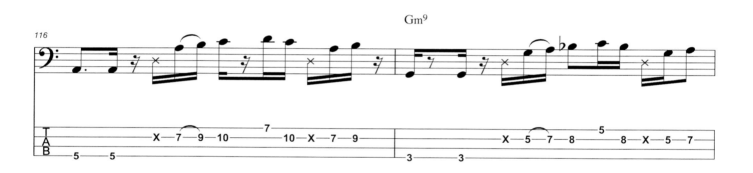

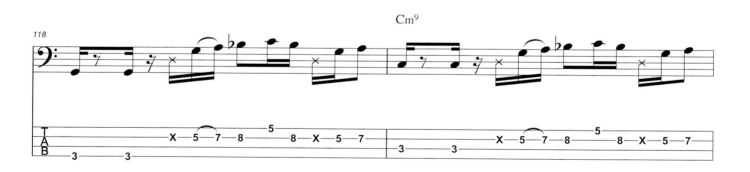

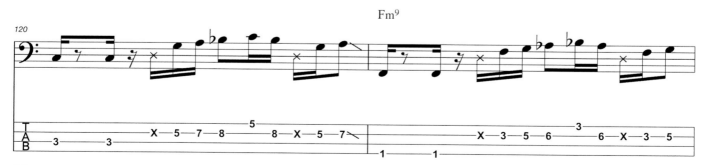

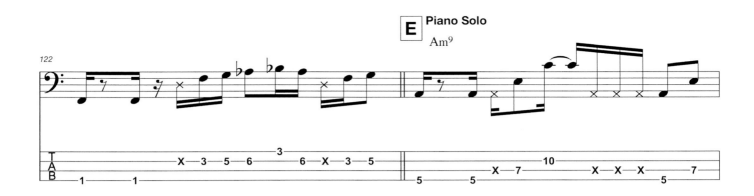

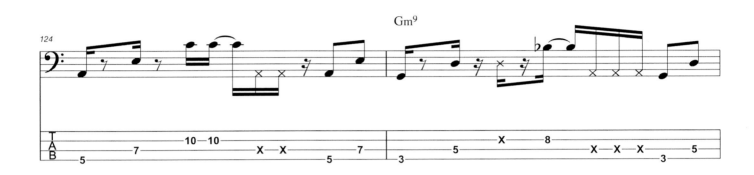

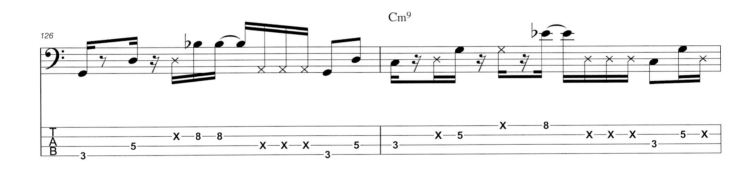

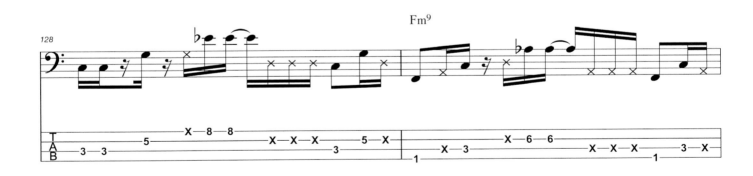

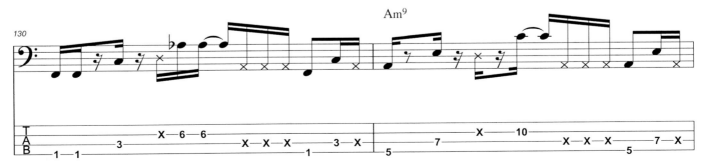

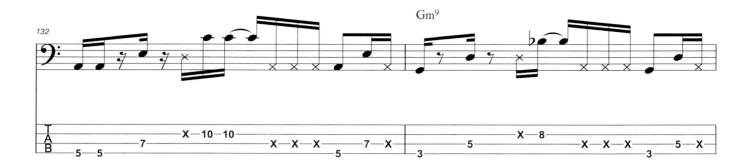

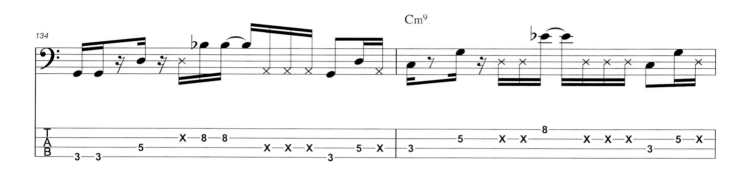

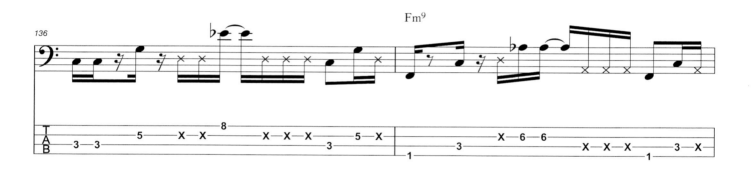

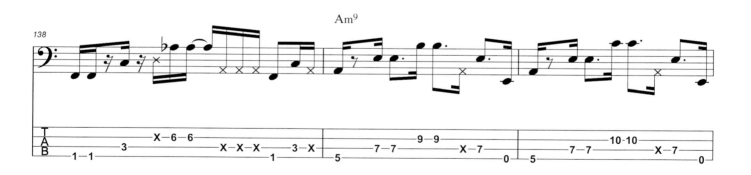

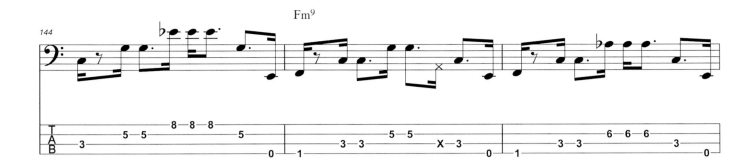

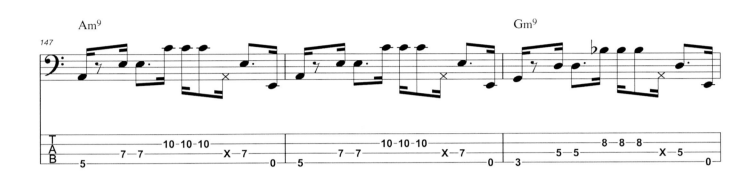

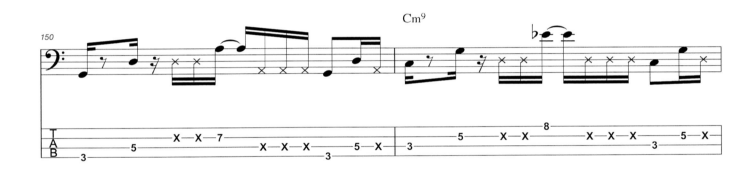

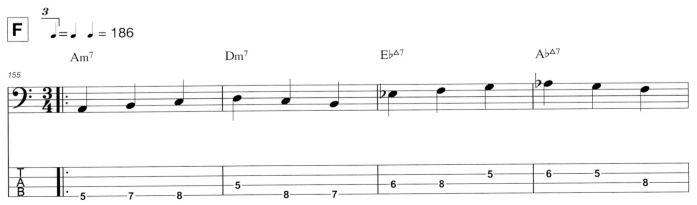

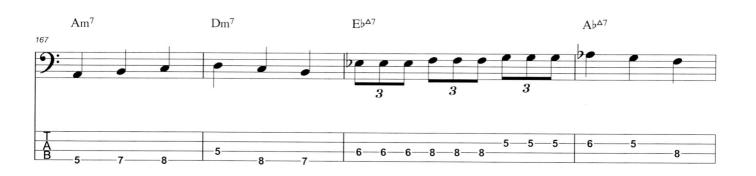

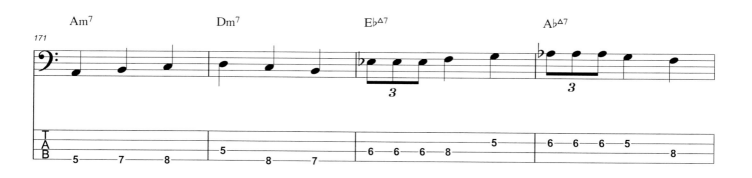

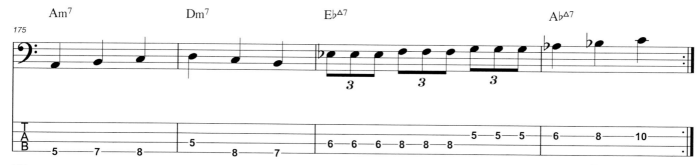

56

Repeat sim to Fade

Emergency on Planet Earth

Written By: Jason Kay/Toby Smith

The title track of the *Emergency on Planet Earth* album is one in which singer Jay Kay reveals his environmentalist leanings. Two versions of the song exist: the album version (which is transcribed here) and an alternative version which features a different intro and bass part. This version can be heard on the greatest hits album *High Times: Singles 1992 - 2006*.

'Emergency on Planet Earth' opens with the guitar and piano outlining the chord progression before the bass and drums enter in the eighth bar. Stuart navigates the fast-moving chord changes with a slapped groove that is predominantly based around root-octave figures. Note the use of inversions in the main groove however: under the B$^{\flat}$7 chord Stuart plays a D (the third of the chord), while under the B$^{\flat}$m^7 chord he plays an A$^{\flat}$ (the seventh). When playing this part be sure to keep notes short where indicated by the staccato dots in the notation.

Stuart continues his line in a similar manner for the Chorus section. Once again, staccato markings should be adhered to closely in order to match the feel of the line, and you should also pay close attention to the use of glissandos (slides).

The two parts discussed so far constitute the majority of the bassline on this song, however, there are some fills and variations that are worthy of your attention: the ghost note fills in bars 32 and 72 are good examples of this.

'Emergency on Planet Earth' was the fourth and final single to be released from the debut album. It was released on 14th August 1993 and remained in the UK Charts for three weeks, peaking at #32. Despite this, it was not often played during the band's early years, and appeared only sporadically in the set-list since then. The group revived it in a heavily re-worked form during their 2017 *Automaton* tour.

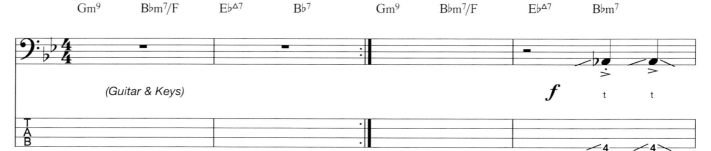

1st Verse

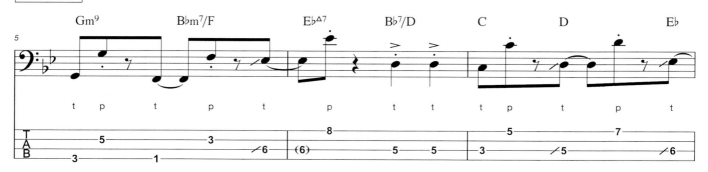

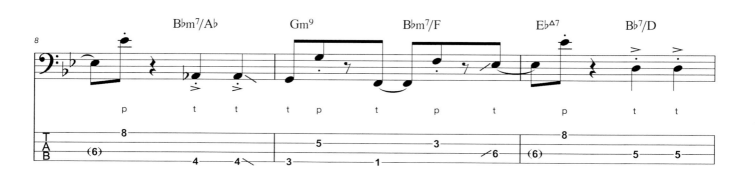

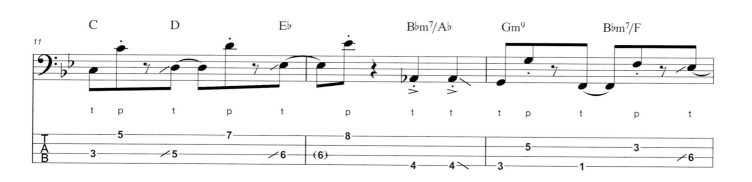

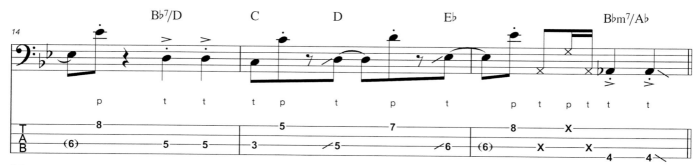

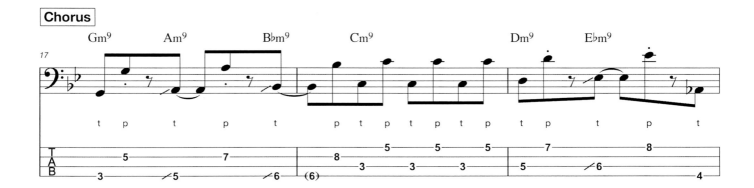

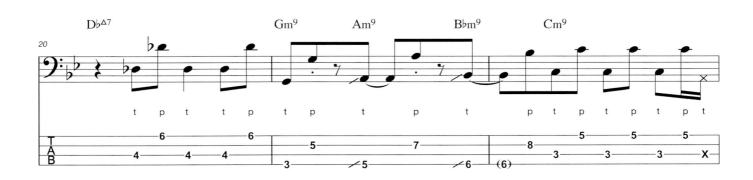

2nd Verse

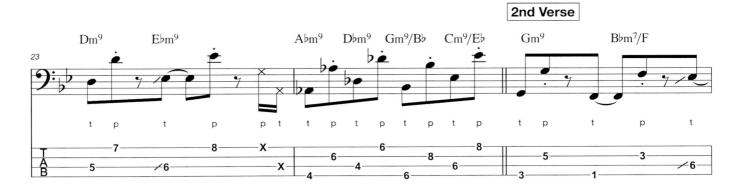

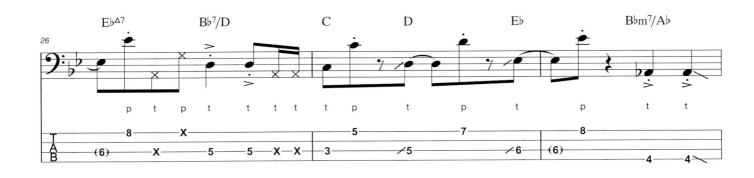

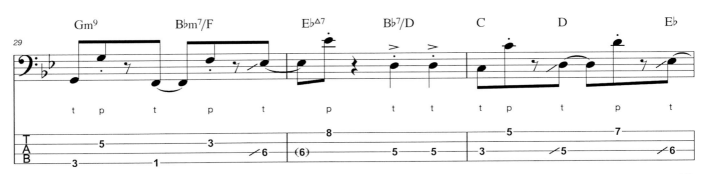

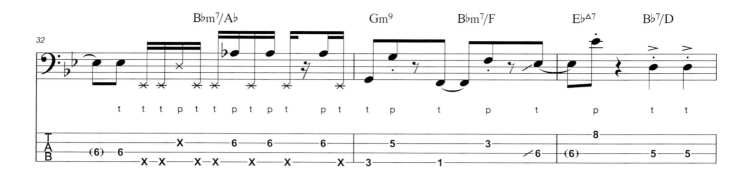

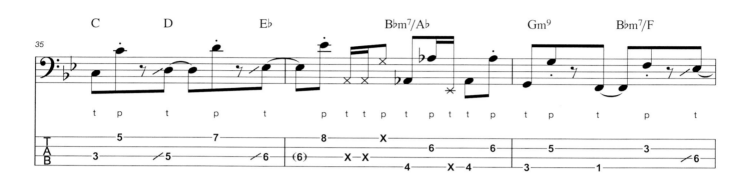

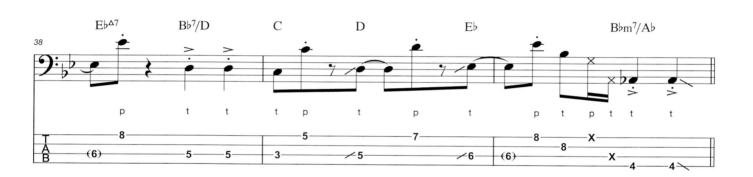

Chorus

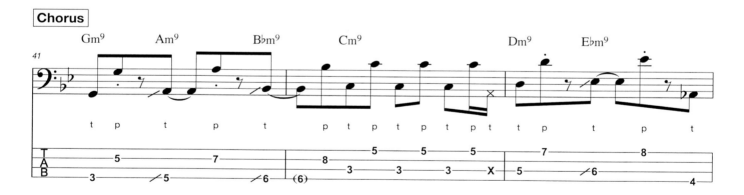

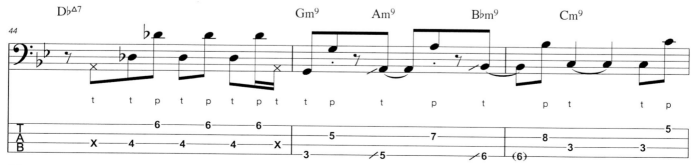

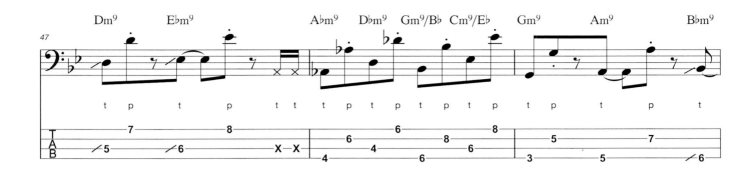

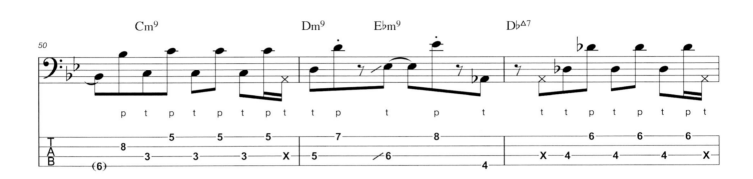

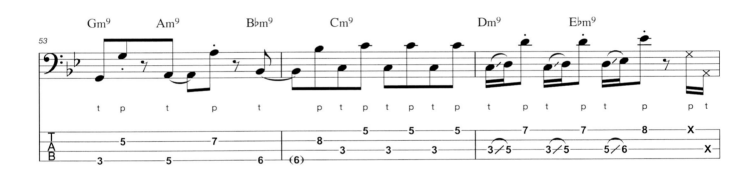

Breakdown

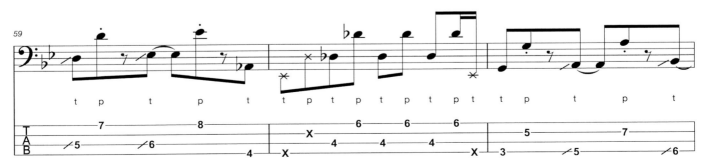

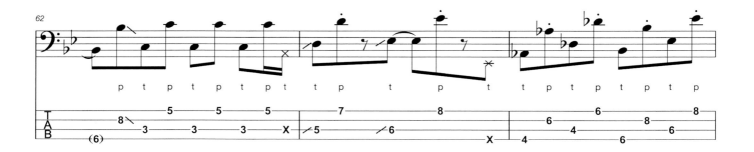

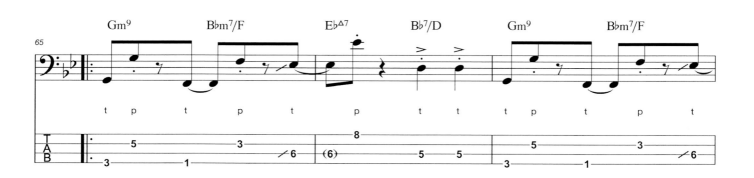

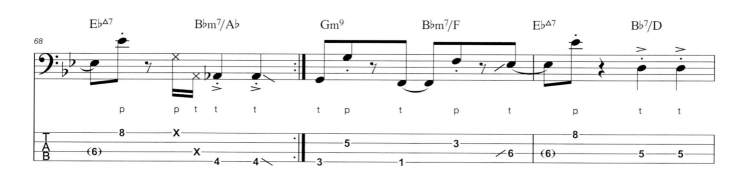

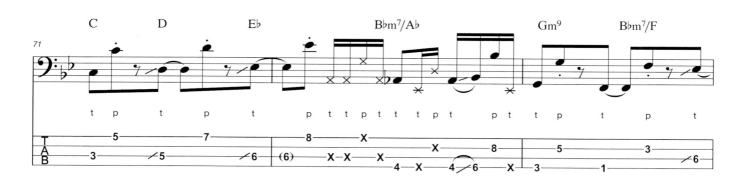

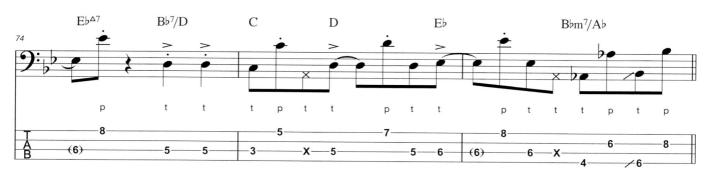

Outro

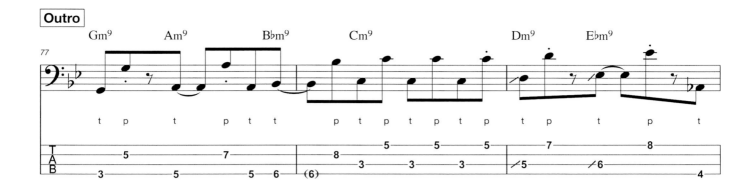

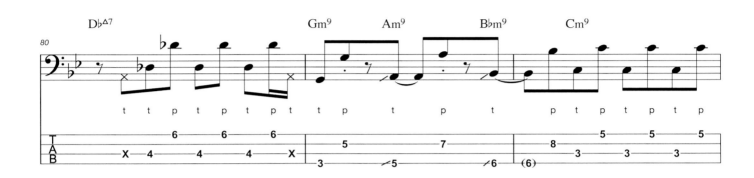

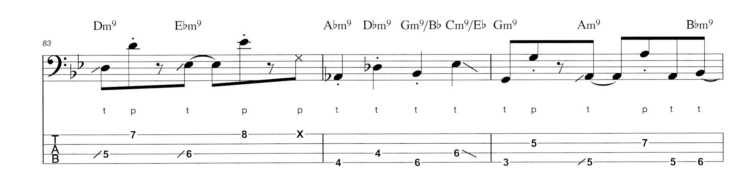

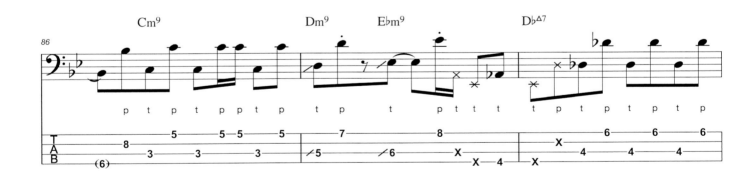

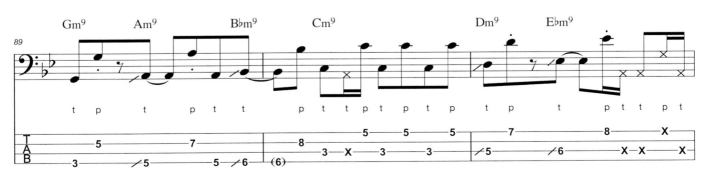

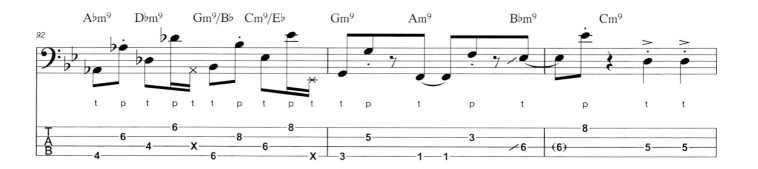

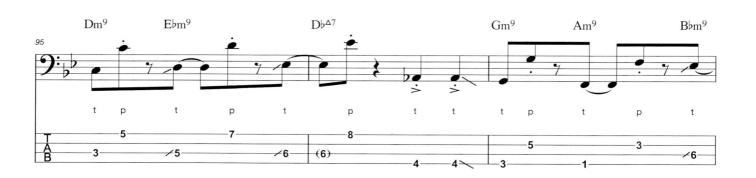

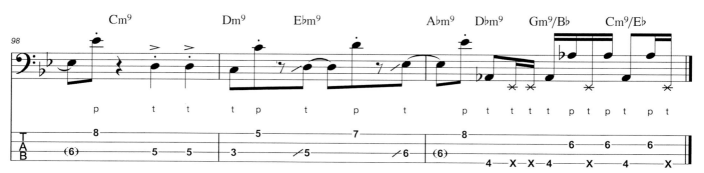

Fade Out

Whatever It Is, I Just Can'

Written By: Jason Kay/Toby Smith

♩ = 98

'Whatever It Is, I Just Can't Stop' is one of the real bass highlights on the *Emergency on I* entire song is based around Stuart Zender's four-bar syncopated funk bassline, which is played throughout the majority of the track, with minimal variation.

The track opens with a four-bar drum groove from Nick Van Gelder, with the bass entering in bar 5. Stuart's line is based on an E Mixolydian framework and his line clearly outlines the suggested E^7 chord which underpins the track. The use of open strings is important when performing this line: in the first bar of the groove, the open D that precedes the run-up to the G♯ is a good example of this. In the second bar of the groove Stuart plays a chromatic ascending line that starts on the third of the chord (G♯) and moves up to the fifth (B). This is played staccato most of the time, but there are a few instances where it is played legato, such as bars 70 and 74 later in the track. In the third bar of the groove Stuart plays an E at the seventh fret of the A-string, then drops quickly to the open E. This is followed by a slide up to the A at the seventh fret of the D-string which is a prelude to a trill on the G - G♯. This is a common funk move, and features the

use of the minor third (G) against a major chord backing. This popular funk idiom hints at the ♯9 (also G), which is a common addition to dominant chords in funk music. Note that Stuart sometimes precedes the trill with a B instead of an A. This line is used for the majority of the song. The only different section is the Bridge, which moves to a C♯7 chord backing and uses a similar line based around C♯.

There are some great funk bass fills in this song. In particular, bars 47-48, 63-64, 71-72, and 79-80 feature some great fills that are worth studying in detail.

This track was recorded on Stuart's Warwick Streamer Stage 1 bass. As you'll be able to hear from the original recording, Stuart digs in quite hard when playing this line, and you should do the same in order to more closely replicate his sound.

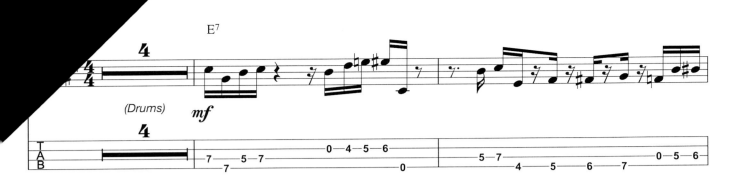

1st Verse

Bridge

C#7

2nd Verse

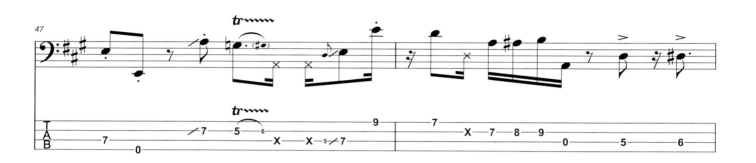

Bridge

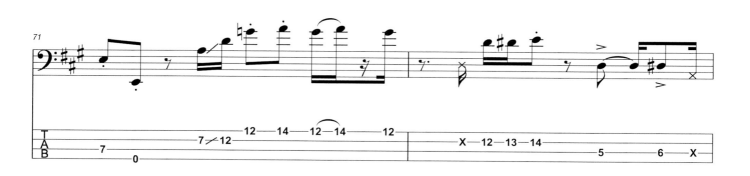

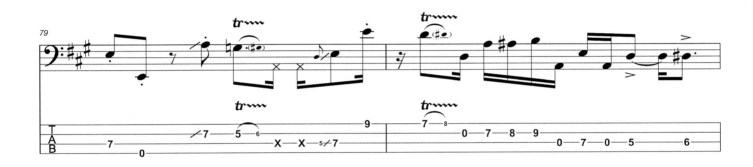

Blow Your Mind

Written By: Jason Kay/Toby Smith

'Blow Your Mind' was the third single to be released from the band's debut album. It was released on 5th June 1993 and spent six weeks in the UK Charts, peaking at #12. Two versions of the song exist: the extended album version, which runs at 8:32, and the much shorter single edit, which clocks in at 3:55 and can be heard on the greatest hits compilation *High Times: Singles 1992 - 2006*. Due to the extensive repetition in the album version of the track, the version transcribed here is the single edit.

'Blow Your Mind' opens with Toby Smith's Rhodes piano, with the band entering after four bars. Stuart immediately sets up a simple - but highly infectious - groove, based around basic chord tones. Staccato markings and the hammer-ons from the open A-string are vital to the feel here. Note the use of a chromatic approach note (B♭ - A) in the second bar of the sequence - this is a subtle touch, but it really adds colour to the line. The repeating two-bar line established in the first Verse is used for the majority of the song.

The chord structure of this track is very simple: the two-bar groove is repeated four times and then transposed up a semitone for another eight bars. This structure is repeated throughout the piece, occasionally broken up by a four-bar accent section - see bars 60 - 63 for an example of this. Note that Stuart adds a couple of harmonics to his C bass note in bar 63, which are a simple but effective touch.

Stuart recorded this track using his Warwick Streamer Stage 1 bass, played through an envelope filter, most likely his Boss ME-6B or ME-8B multi-effects unit. The envelope effect is quite subtle and easily missed, but it certainly adds some funk 'squelch' to the line.

'Blow Your Mind' was an important part of the band's set in the early days, and continues to feature in the set-list from time to time.

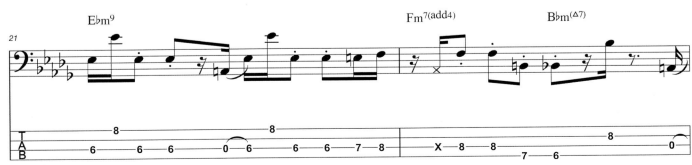

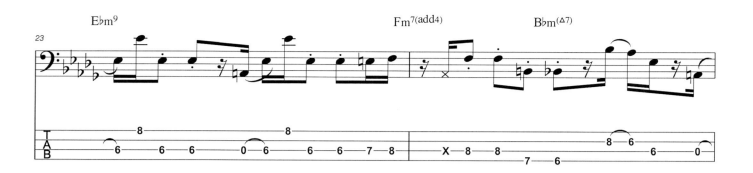

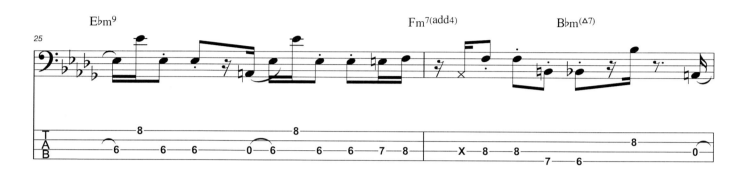

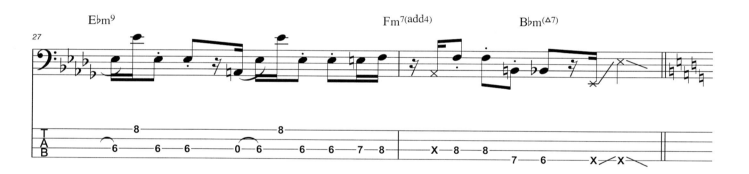

2nd Verse

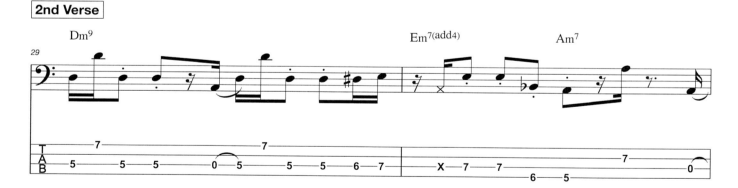

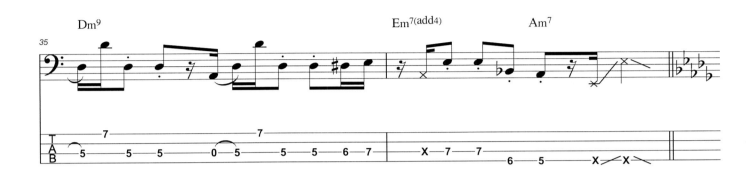

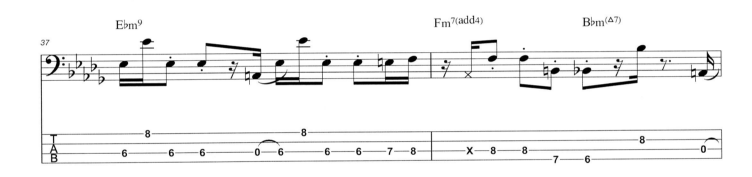

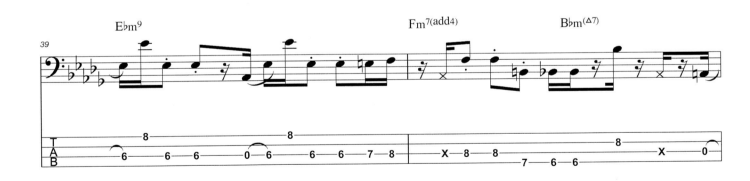

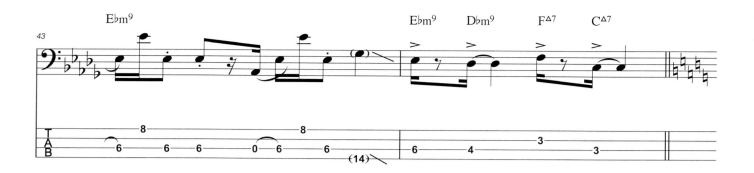

3rd Verse

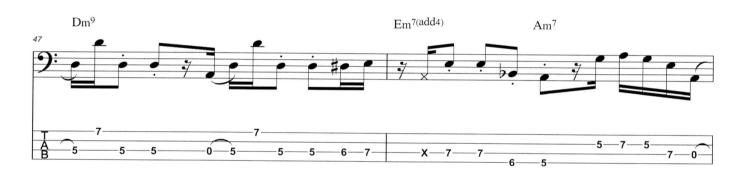

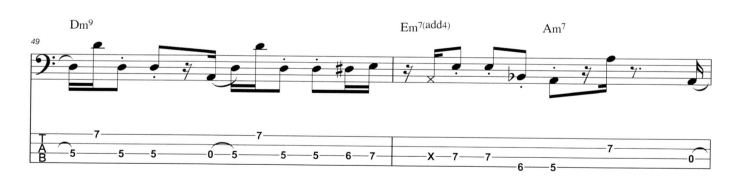

80

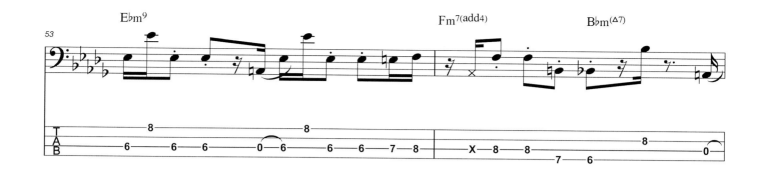

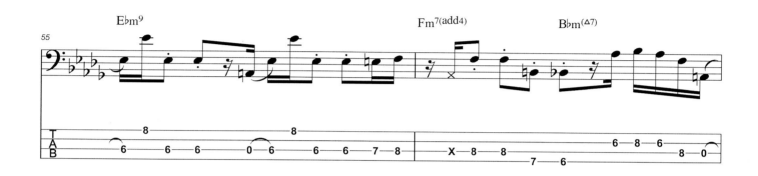

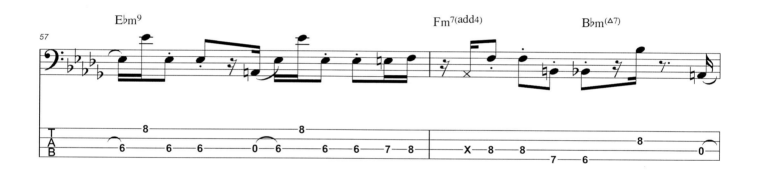

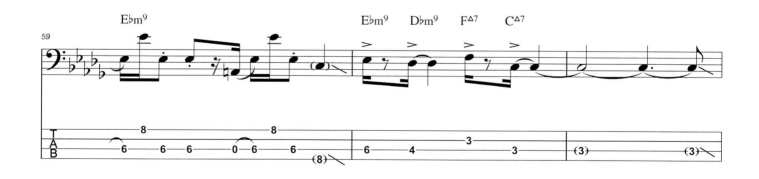

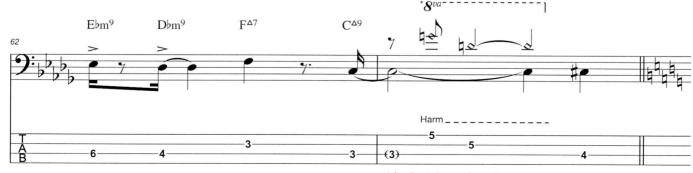

* Applies to harmonics only

4th Verse

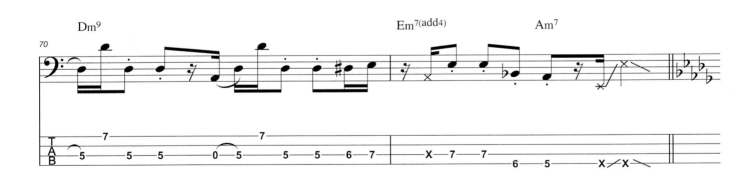

82

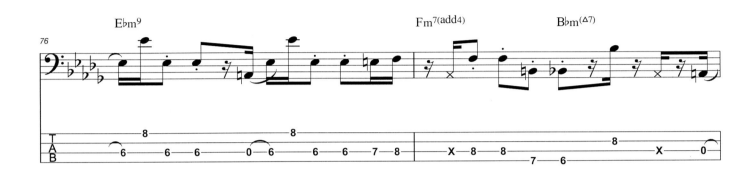

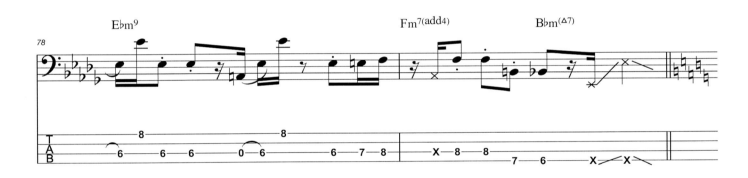

Vocal/Trumpet Solo

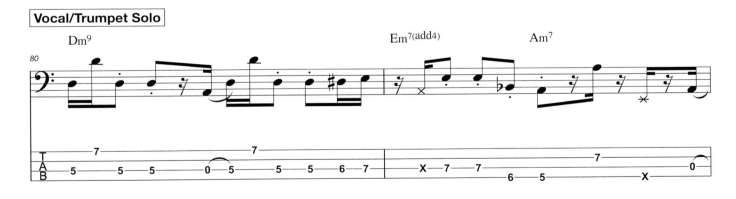

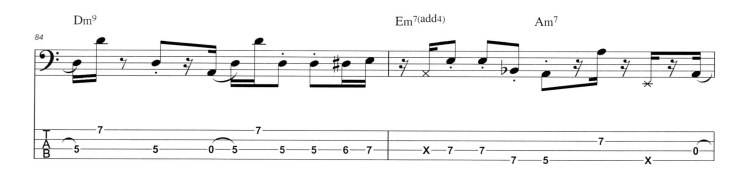

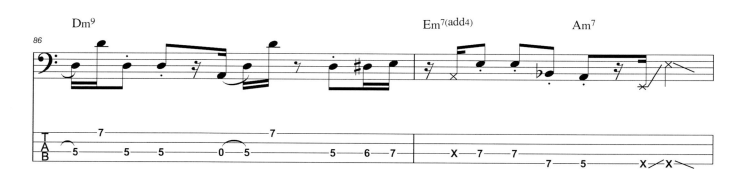

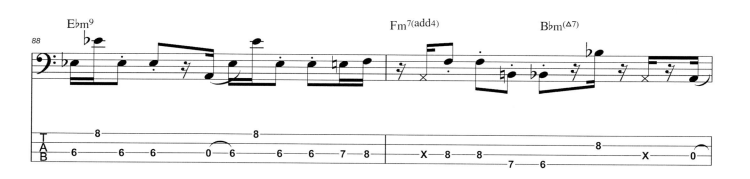

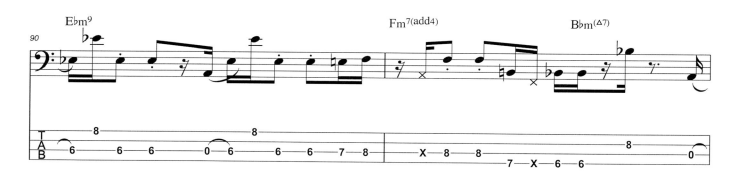

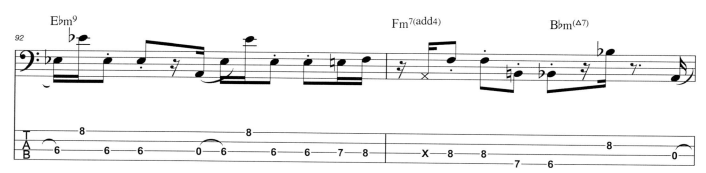

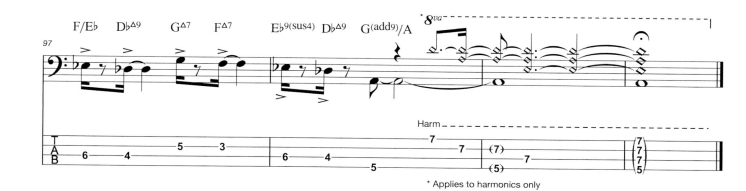

* Applies to harmonics only

Another Story

y/Toby Smith

'Just Another Story' is the opening track from the band's second album *The Return of the Space Cowboy*. With a running time of 8:50 it is one of the band's longer compositions and features superb performances from all concerned, particularly Stuart Zender, whose heavily effected bass grooves provide a perfect foundation.

Despite Jay Kay's protestations that 'This is not another trilogy…' this is nevertheless a song in three parts. The first section - which some consider to be an 'overture' of sorts to the album as a whole - is a largely instrumental piece that features Stuart using a Boss ME-8B multi-effects unit to create slippery upper-register lines. The sound heard here can be replicated with a Mutron pedal, or any other similar envelope filter pedal. The bass enters in bar 15, doubling the already established melody line. Note the use of ghost notes, slides and vibrato here, all crucial to recreating the line as Stuart played it. In bar 19 Stuart settles into a groove that finds him moving from the low end of the instrument right to the very top - the G at the 24th fret of the G-string (if your bass does not have a full twenty-four fret range then you will need to play this part an octave lower). This upper register motif is followed by two groups of descending notes, one on the G-string, the other on the E-string. Stuart continues this line, with embellishments for the remainder of this first section of the tune.

At CD time 2:23 the second part of the song begins with Toby Smith's Rhodes piano riff. This is doubled by the bass when it enters in bar 61. Stuart plays an upper register string rake in the preceding bar (60). This is a rhythmic flourish rather than a melodic one and it is

therefore not important which pitches are struck on the lower strings. The important thing is to get the rhythmic 'rake' across the strings, followed by the glissando (slide) downwards. Throughout this second section, Stuart doubles the keys riff, and fills the two-bar gaps with fills. Check out the cool bluesy fill in bars 95-96 and the slippery line in bars 111-112 for two great examples. At bar 133 the song shifts to a different set of chord changes and Stuart continues with the same format, moving it upwards through the chord progression accordingly.

Beginning in bar 149 is the third and final section of the track. This begins with a flute solo under which Stuart plays legato glissando figures. Whilst the chord progression used here is the same as the previous section, Stuart now creates a completely new line, using chord tones to outline each chord and syncopating the part heavily. This line suggests the influence of great funk players such as Jaco Pastorius and Bernard Edwards in his playing. The track ends with an ascending chromatic unison line.

This song has been performed live on many occasions, often without the first 'overture' section. It was most recently played on some shows during the *Rock Dust Light Star* tour in 2010.

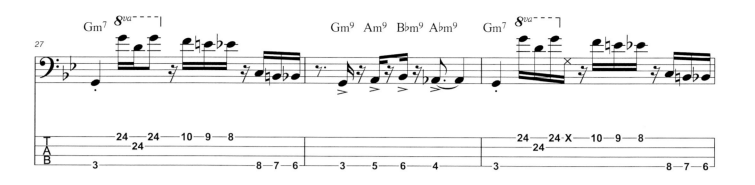

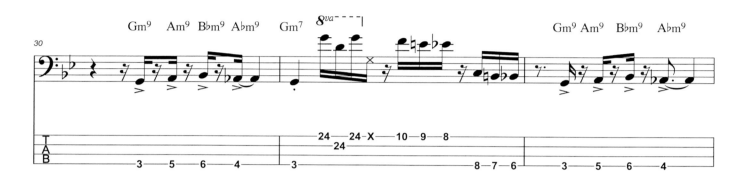

1st Verse

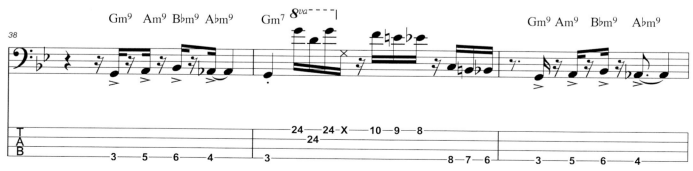

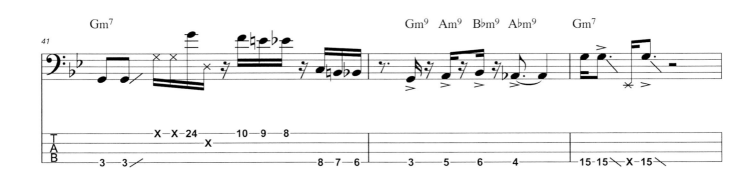

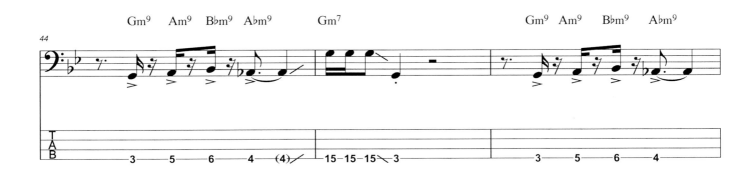

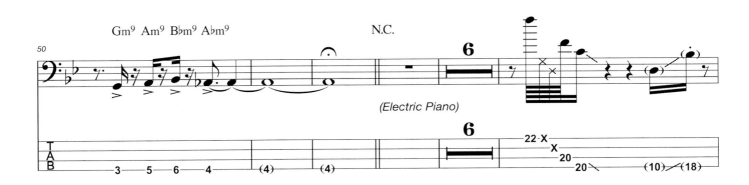

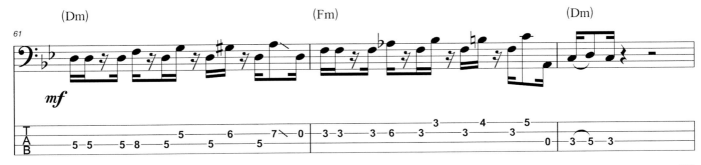

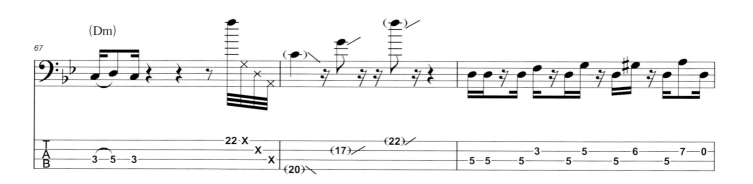

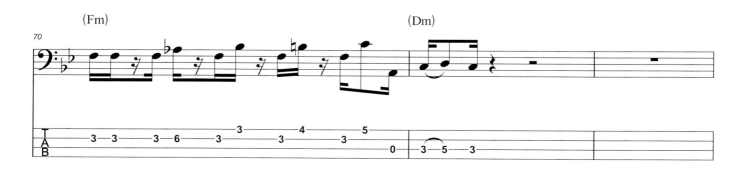

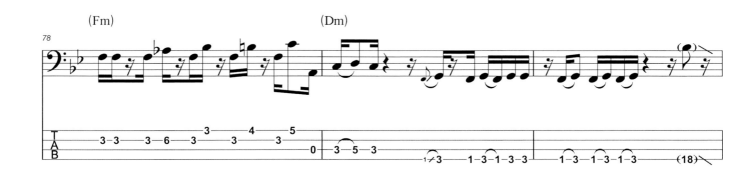

2nd Verse

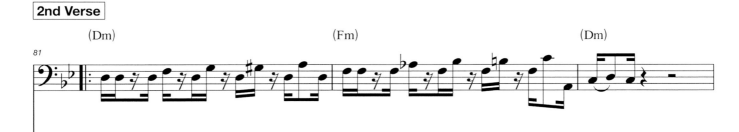

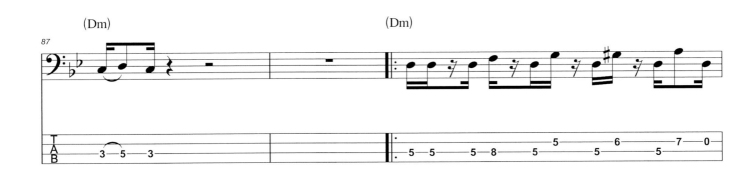

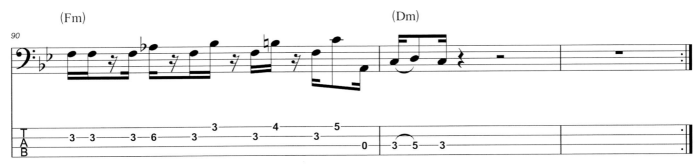

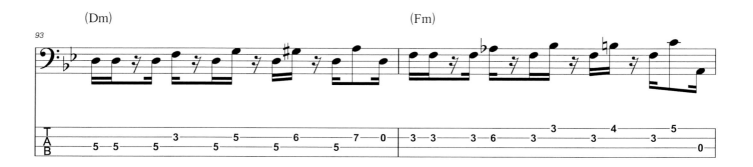

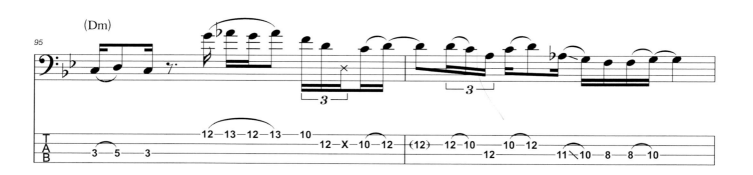

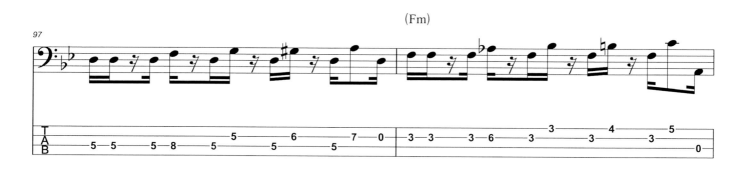

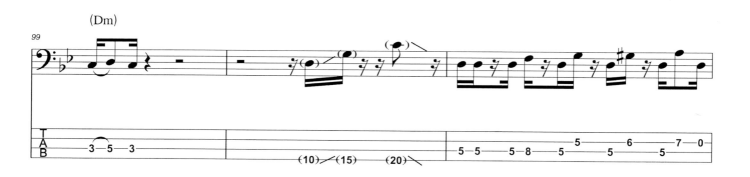

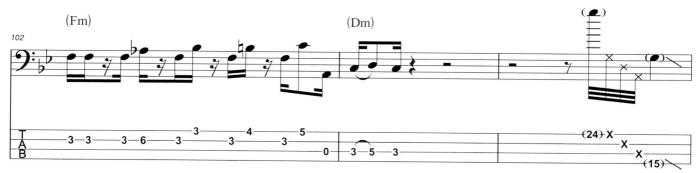

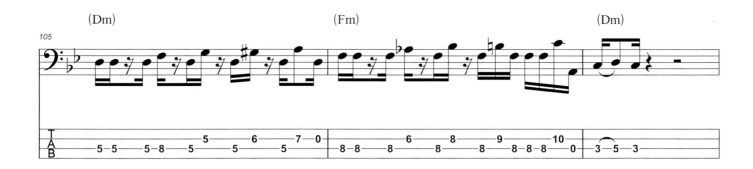

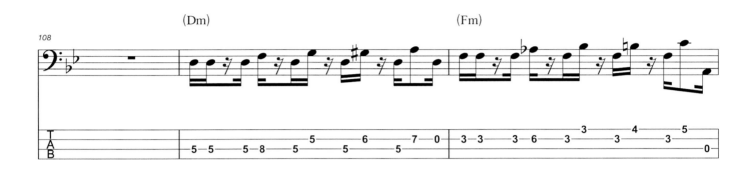

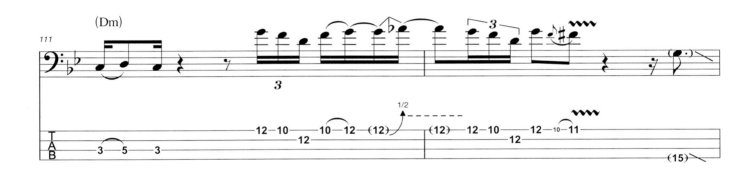

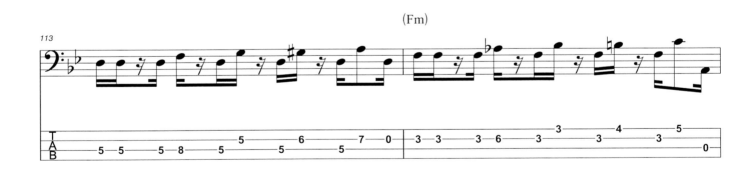

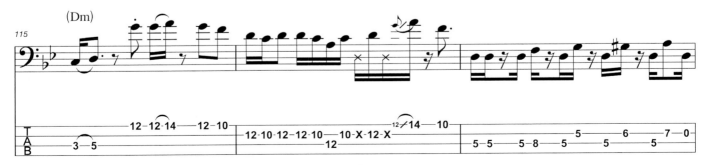

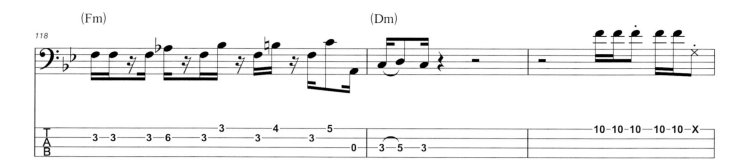

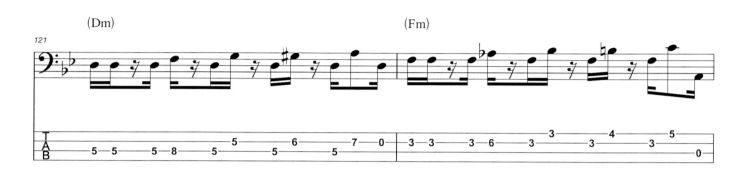

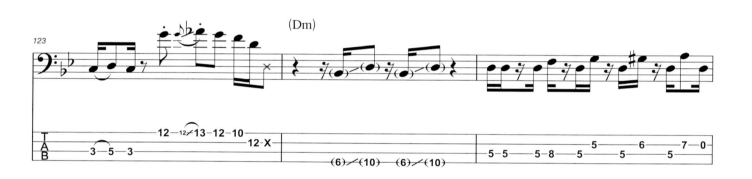

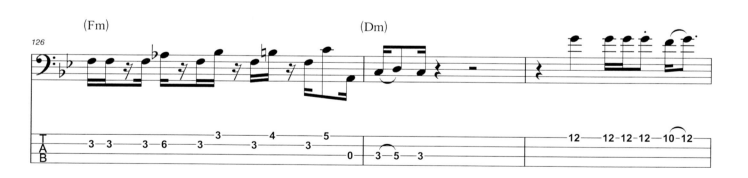

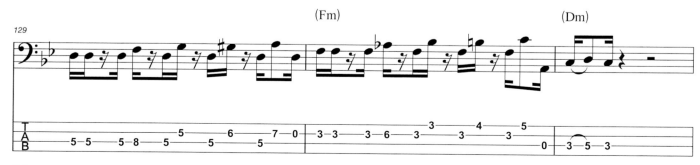

Chorus

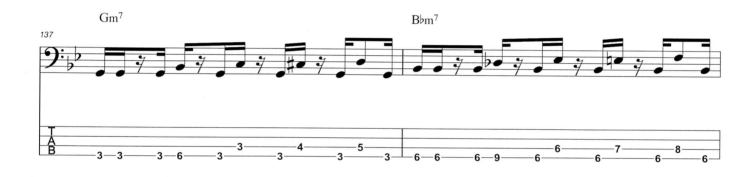

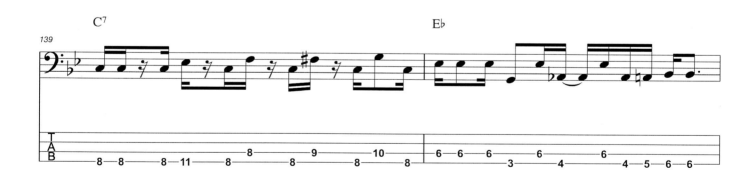

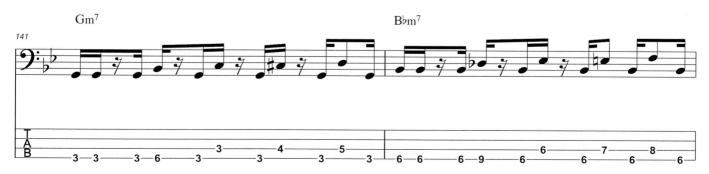

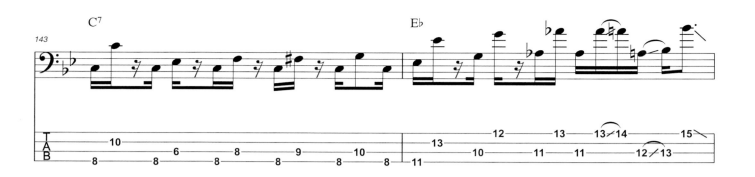

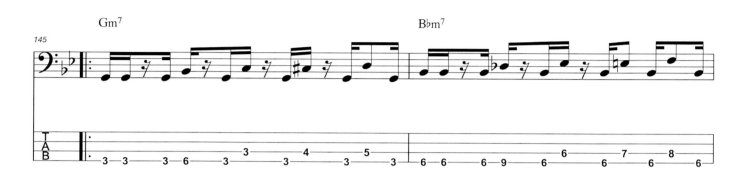

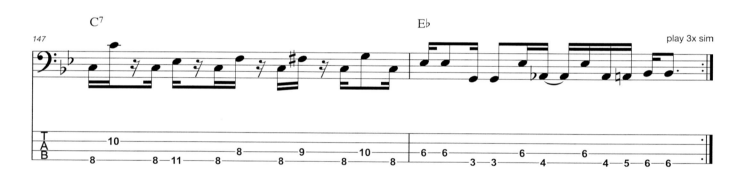

Flute Solo

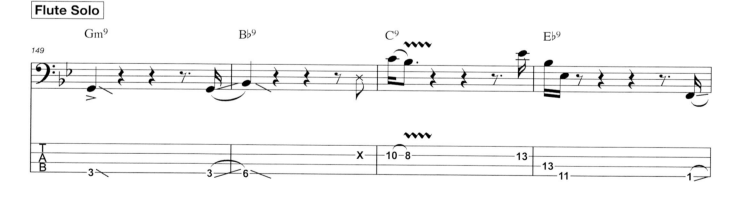

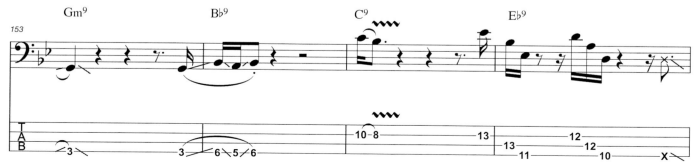

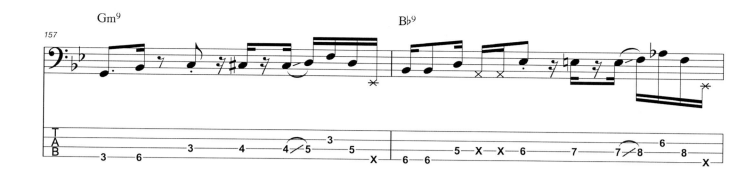

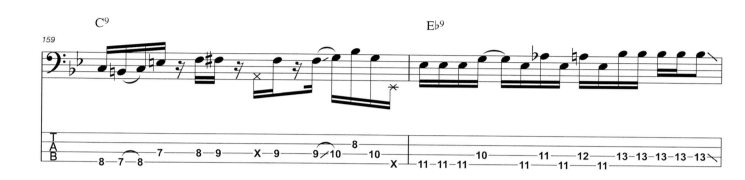

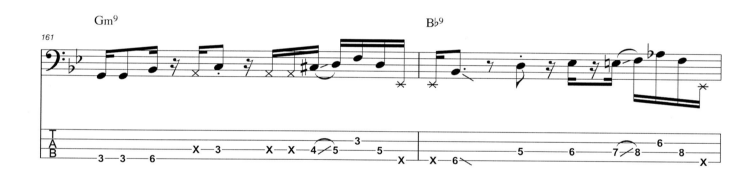

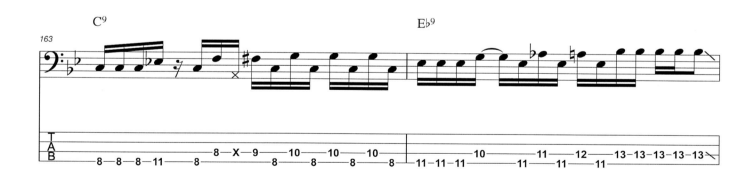

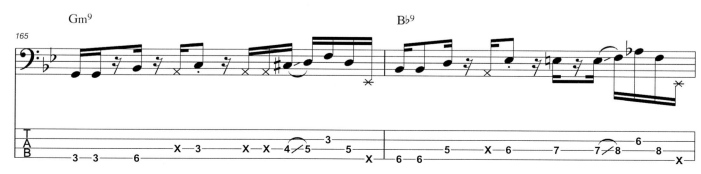

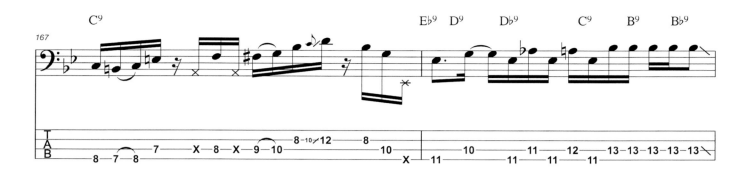

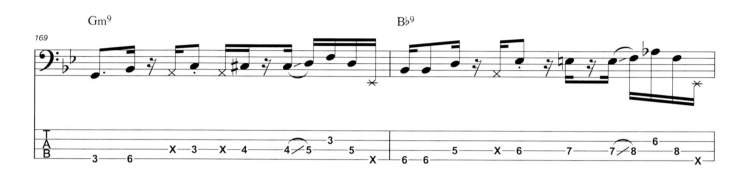

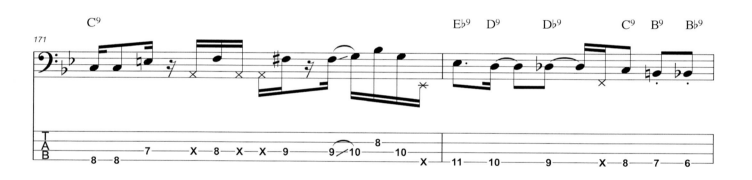

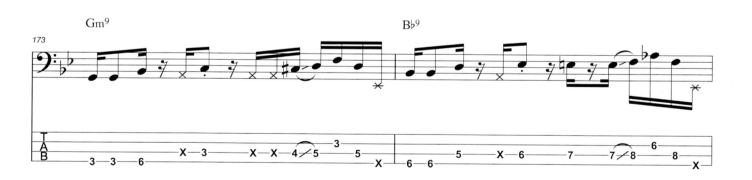

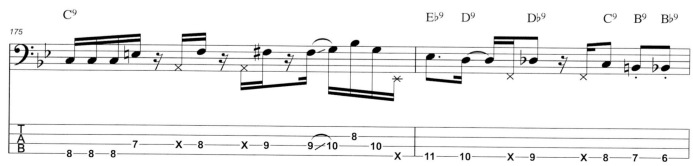

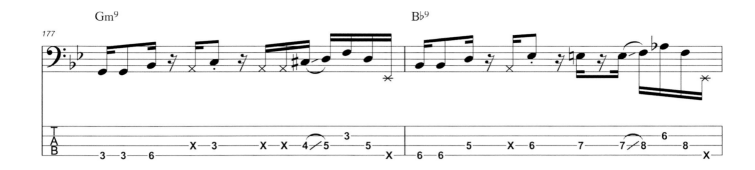

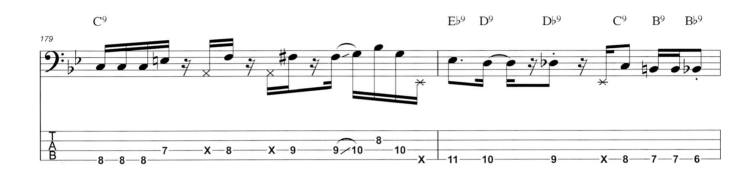

Outro

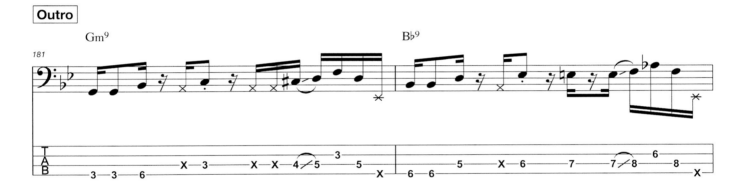

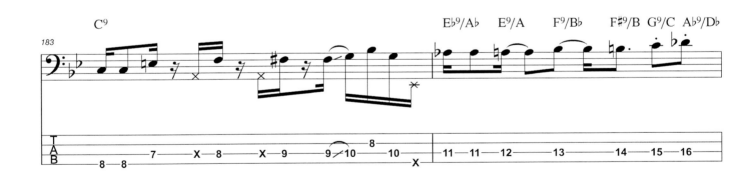

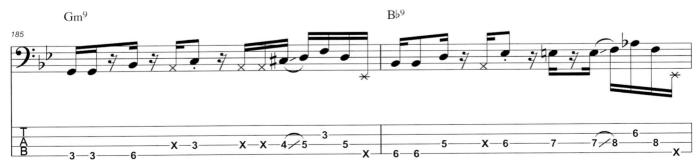

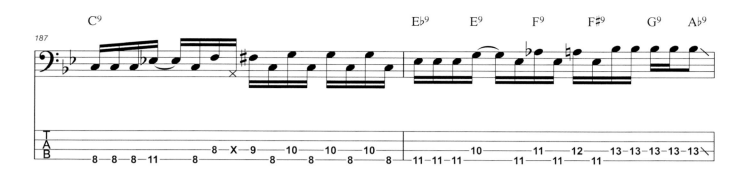

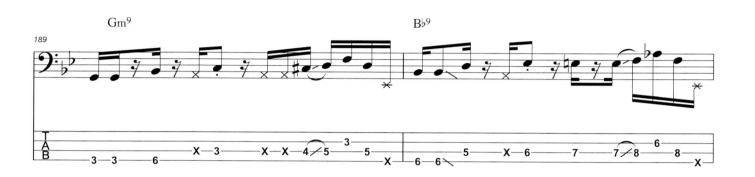

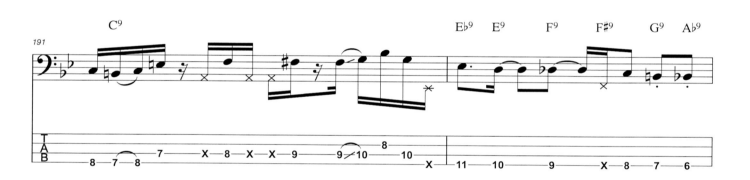

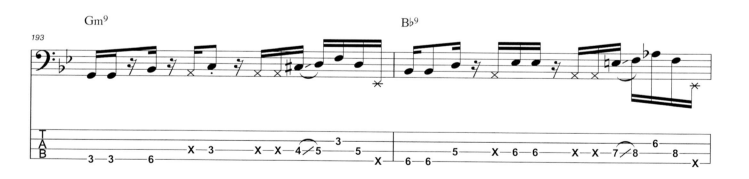

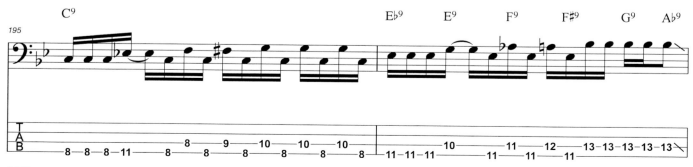

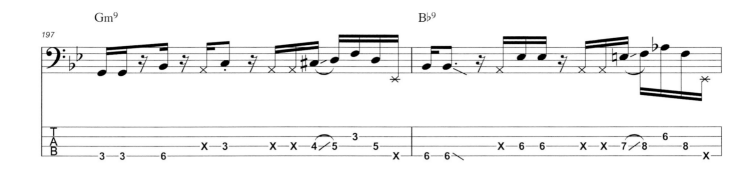

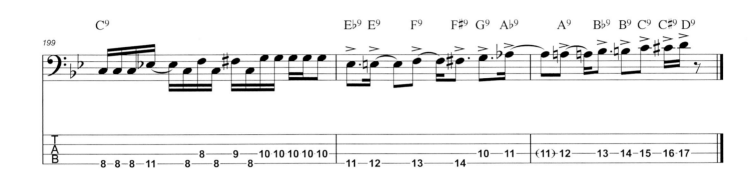

Stillness In Time

Written By: Jason Kay/Toby Smith

'Stillness in Time' was the third single to be released from the *Return of the Space Cowboy* album, following 'Space Cowboy' and 'Half the Man'. It was released on 1st July 1995 and spent five weeks in the UK charts, peaking at #9. The album version of this track is 4:17 in length, with the single being an edited version that was cut down to 3:43. A longer version was released on the vinyl edition of the album, clocking in at 6:13. The CD album version has been transcribed here.

'Stillness in Time' is a light pop track that features a busy chord progression ably supported by a fluid bassline from Stuart Zender. There are three distinct 'sections' to the track: the first Verse (an eight-bar section), the second Verse (another eight bar section with a different chord progression) and the Chorus, which is a repeating two-bar chord progression which is capped off with a unison line first heard at CD time 1:27.

Throughout the song, Stuart's bassline is heavily based on chord tones, focusing predominantly on a root-fifth movement. This is often embellished to include the ninth of the chord such as in the first bar, where he plays the root of the F^9 chord (F), the fifth (C), and the ninth (G). This is a common bass figure – particularly in jazz-funk lines – and is one that Stuart frequently revisits during the song.

When performing this line be sure to note the use of staccato markings in the notation (used to indicate that a note should be kept very short) and rests. Both are important to the feel of this line and you should take time to play the line exactly as written - listen to Stuart's performance for guidance. You will also notice the use of ghost notes throughout this bassline - these are again very important to the feel, and need to be played where written. Ghost notes are written on the string where it is most logical to play them, although as they are essentially pitch-less notes, it technically does not matter where they are played.

This track was only occasionally played live by the band and hasn't been heard in their set since a single performance at the Lovebox Festival in 2006.

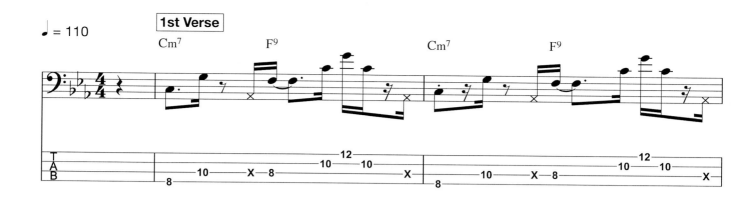

1st Verse

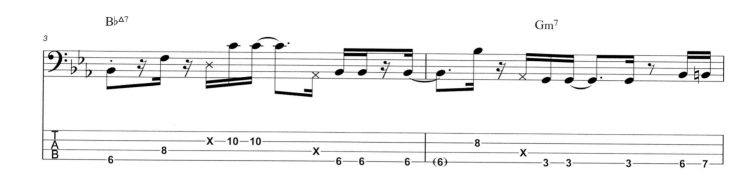

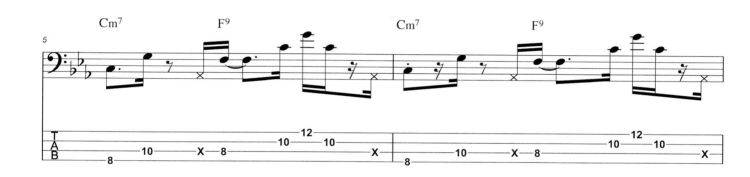

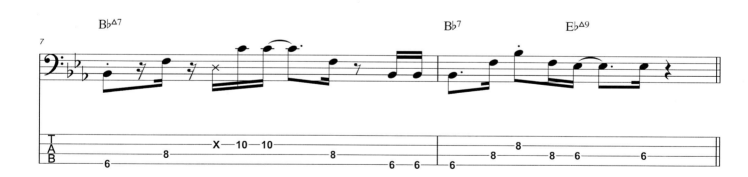

2nd Verse

103

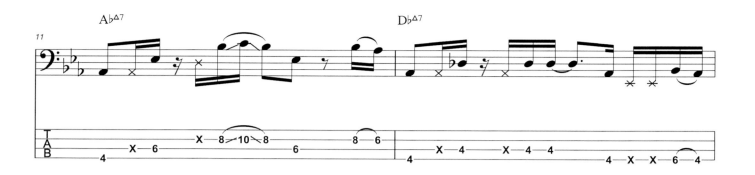

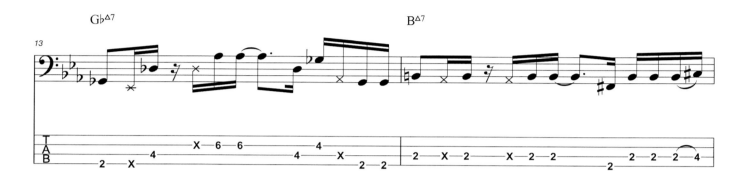

3rd Verse

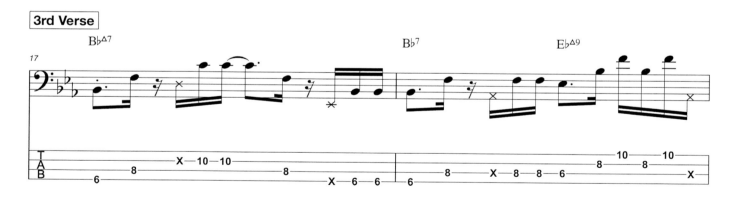

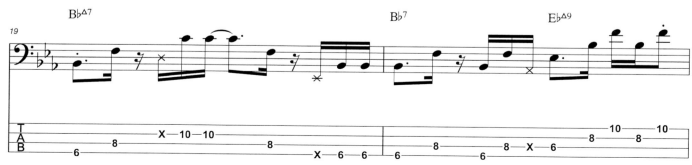

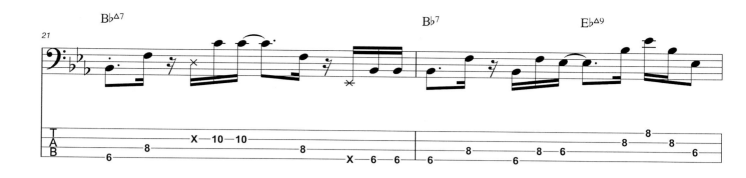

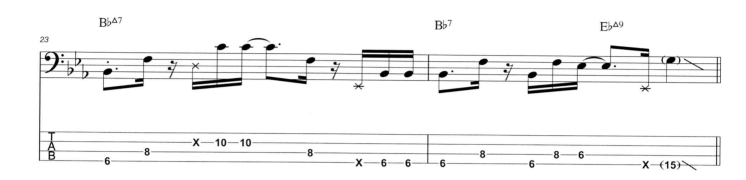

Chorus

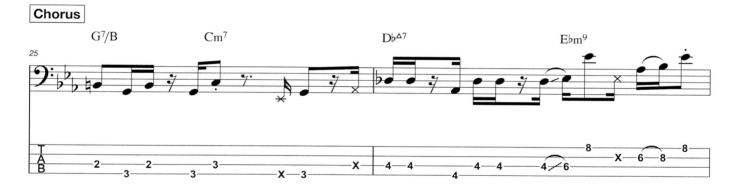

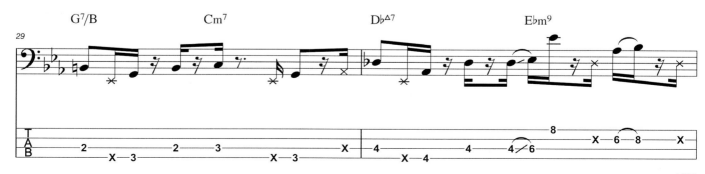

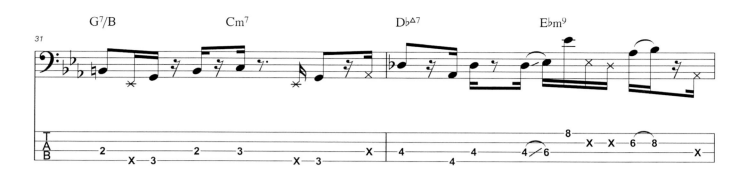

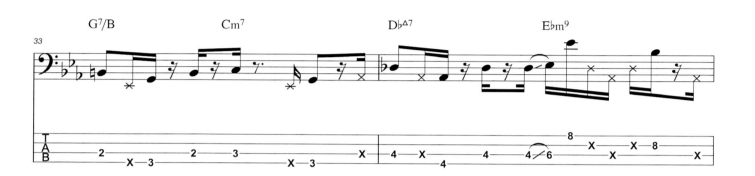

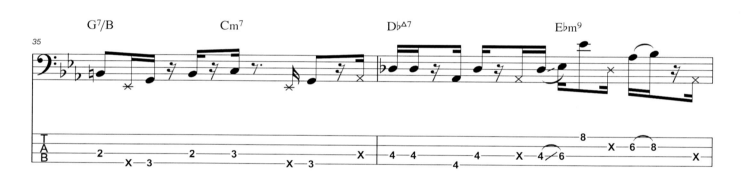

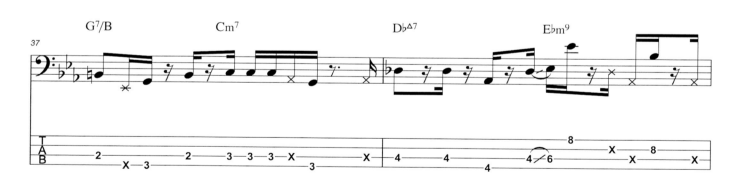

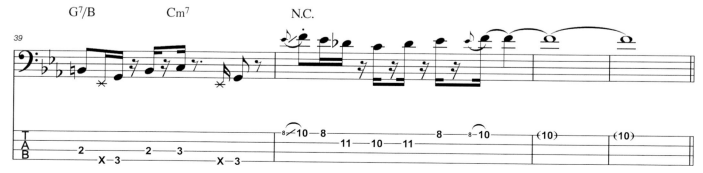

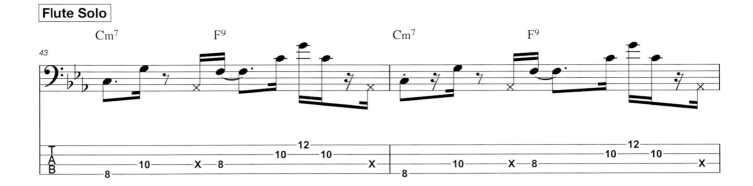

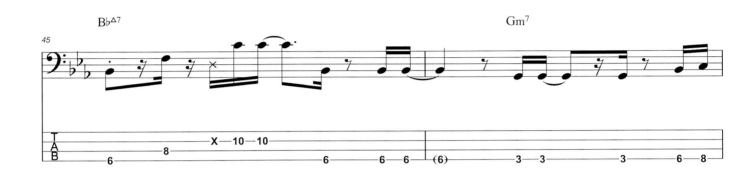

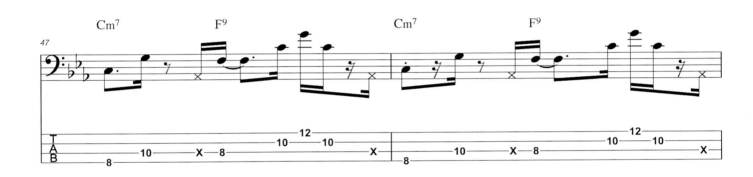

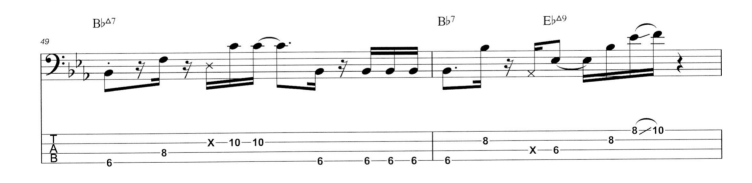

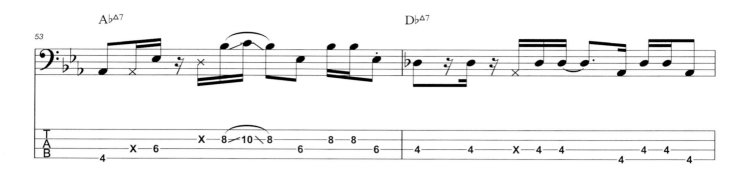

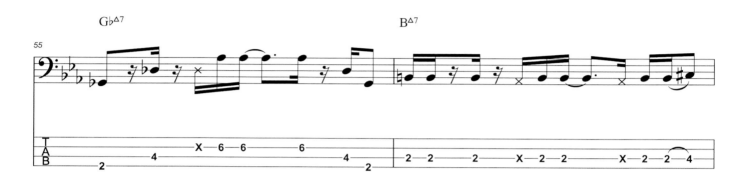

4th Verse

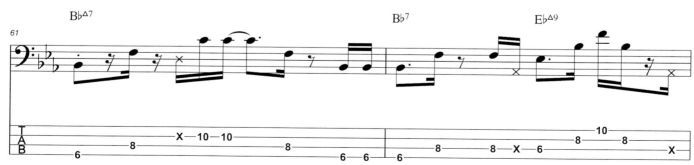

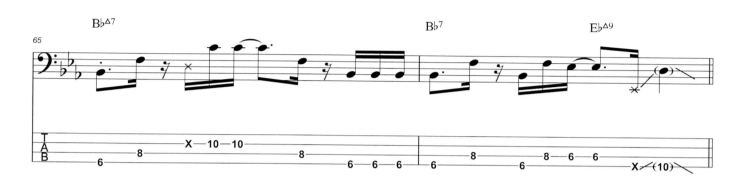

Chorus

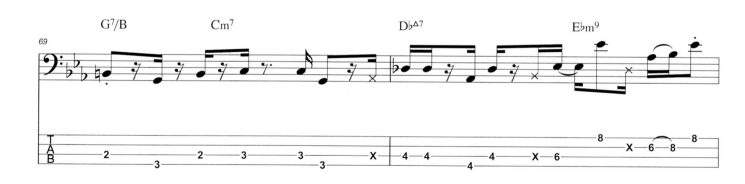

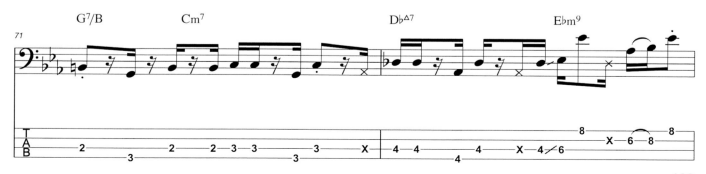

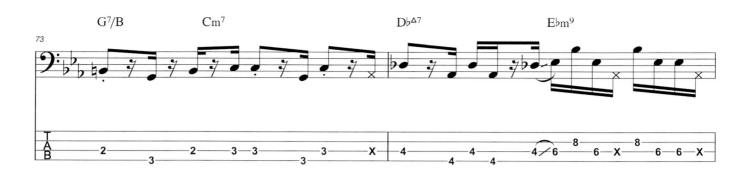

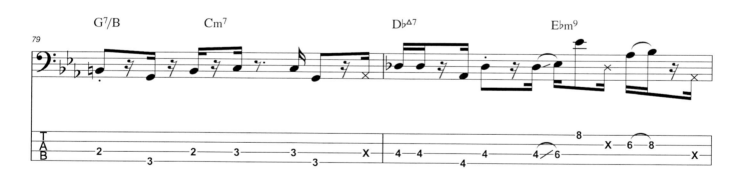

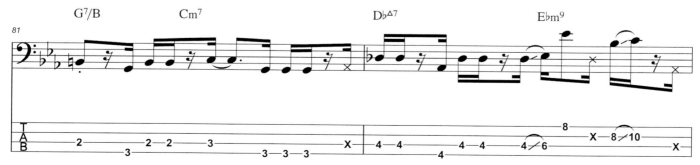

110

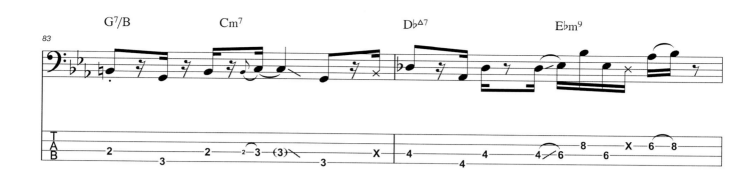

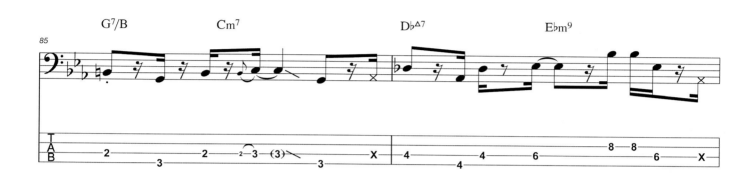

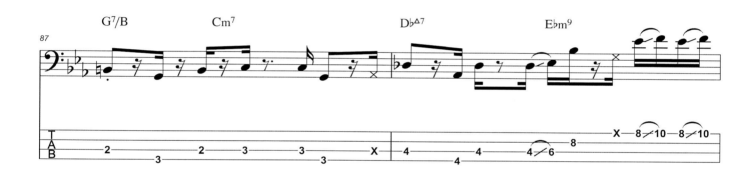

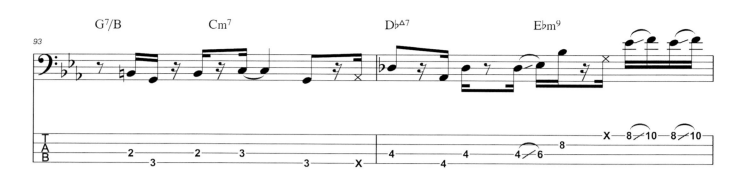

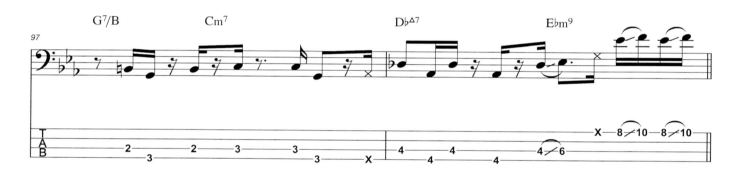

Outro

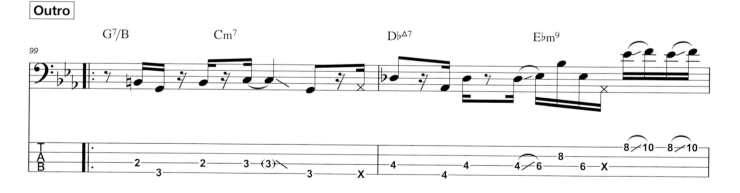

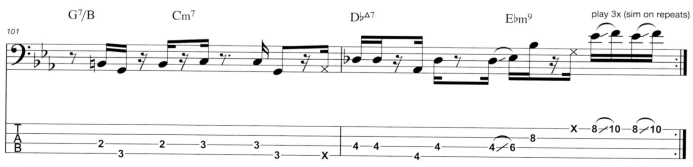

112

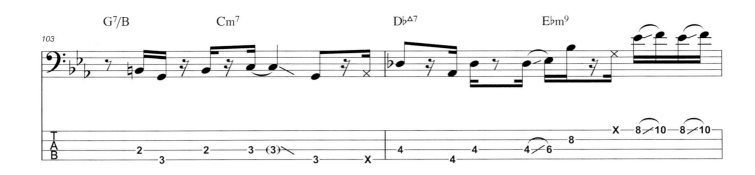

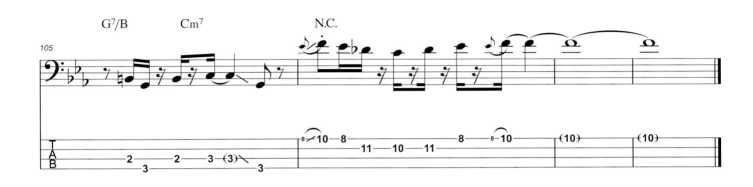

Light Years

Written By: Jason Kay/Toby Smith

'Light Years' is an unusual song that nevertheless features some great bass playing from Stuart Zender – in particular, it is notable for his use of a fuzz pedal to create a dirty, synth-like tone during the Verse sections. This track was the fourth single to be released from the *Return of the Space Cowboy* album, although it did not fare well on the charts, peaking only at #36. Two versions of the song exist: the album version - which is transcribed here - and a shorter edit which was released as the single.

'Light Years' is predominantly based around an E minor pentatonic piano riff which repeats throughout the majority of the song. The bass does not enter until CD Time 0:22 (written as bar 5), where Stuart plays a descending E minor figure using his fuzz pedal. Note that pitches are indicated in brackets here as they are somewhat indistinct. Throughout the Verse section of the tune Stuart doubles parts of the piano riff in the upper register, and plays these lower register staccato lines. The bass sound here is huge, with the fuzz only adding more weight. Beginning in bar 12 a long unison figure is played by the band. This too is based on the E minor pentatonic scale and contains a lot of heavily syncopated notes and a 7/8 bar, all of which make this a tricky part to play. This is followed by a second Verse, during which Stuart continues to play in the same vein.

The Chorus, when it arrives in bar 33, is a notable change of mood and is based around a simple two-bar chord sequence. Stuart switches to a regular bass sound at this point, playing a simple but effective line that is full of great fills and rhythmic ideas. His use of staccato and ghost notes is as impressive as ever and his upper register fill in bar 41 is a great touch.

The two parts discussed above are used throughout the song, although there are many variations on the Chorus sections. The fills in bars 79 and 87 are certainly worthy of your attention.

'Light Years' has been performed live on many occasions and was most recently heard at the Paleo Festival in 2010.

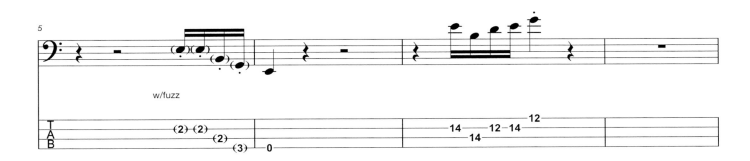

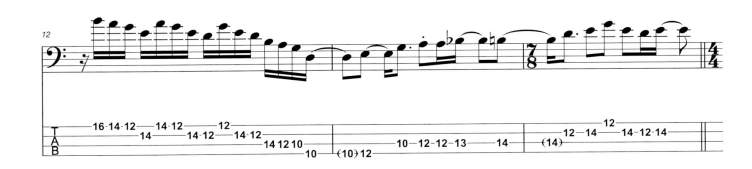

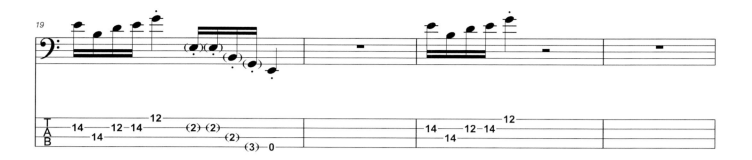

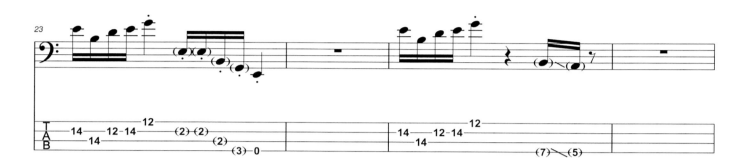

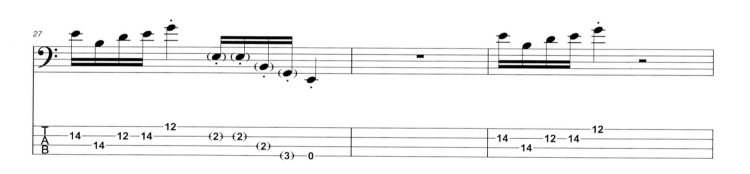

Chorus

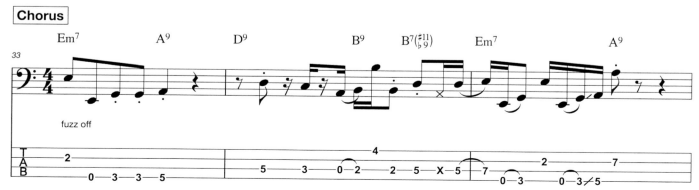

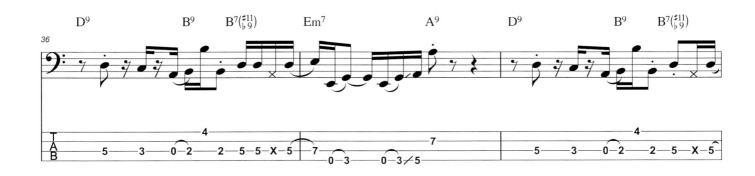

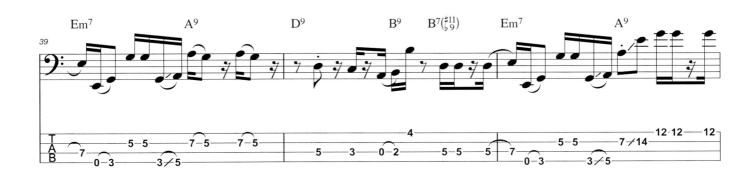

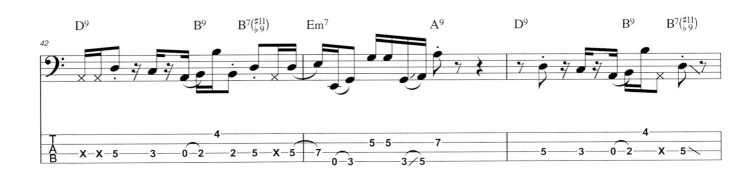

3rd Verse

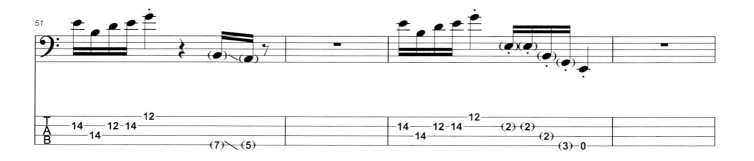

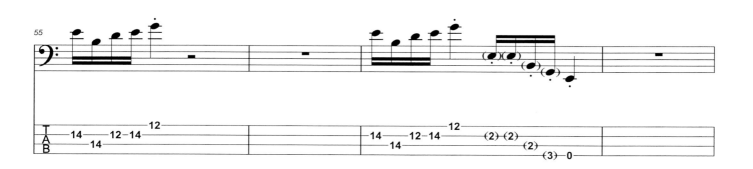

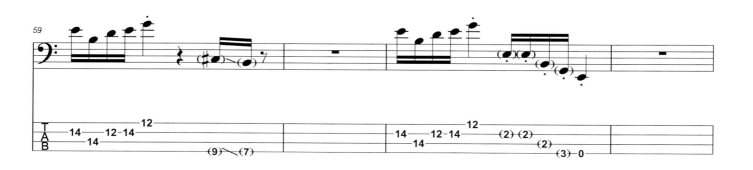

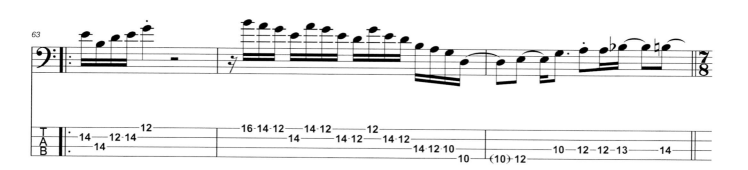

Chorus

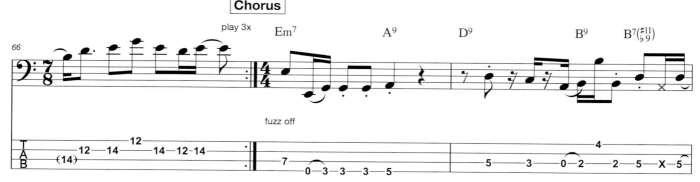

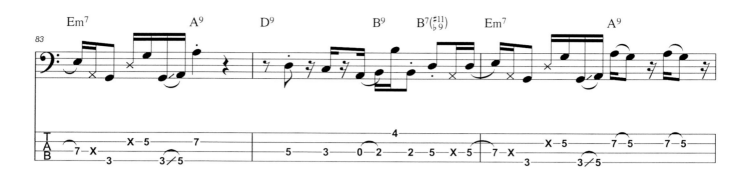

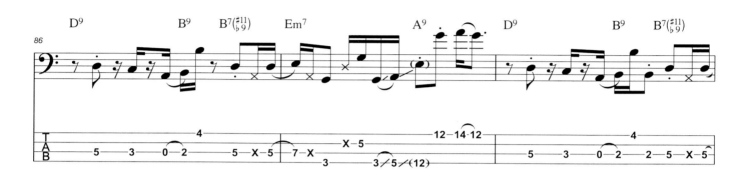

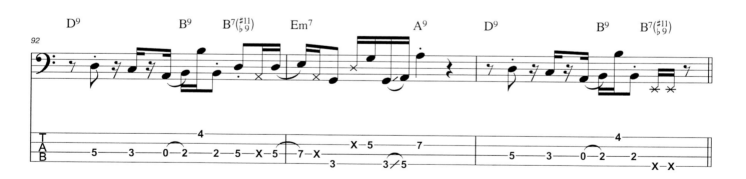

Breakdown

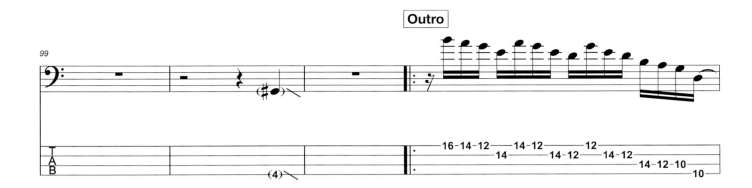

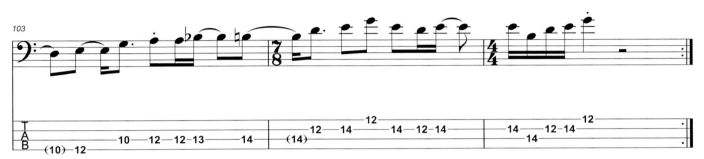

Repeat to Fade

Manifest Destiny

Written By: Jason Kay/Toby Smith

'Manifest Destiny' is a popular Jamiroquai song amongst fans of bassist Stuart Zender. The song features a distinctive, melodic bass part for the Verse sections that is undoubtedly one of the album's bass guitar highlights.

The song opens with Stuart's melodic line, which clearly outlines the chord progression that is used for the Verse sections. The first bar is predominantly based around chord tones from Bm7 (B, D, F♯, A), and ends on an A♯, the third of the F#7 chord in the second bar. Playing the third instead of the root note here is a nice touch and is far less predictable. Note that the open A-string in this bar is really just used as a jumping off point for the F♯ - G - F♯ figure. The F♯ here is obviously the root of the chord, whilst the G implies a flattened ninth. In the third bar Stuart clearly outlines an Em9 sound (E, G, B, D, F♯) and the fourth bar of the sequence is a melodic turnaround figure. This Intro melody is played twice before the rest of the band enters. On the second playing, there is a ghost note fill in the second bar of the sequence (see bar 6). This is played by raking back across the strings with a right hand finger. This is a very effective rhythmic device, and Stuart uses it often in his playing. Other examples can be found in 'Just Another Story', which was transcribed earlier in this book.

The Chorus sections of this song are based around a different 4-bar chord structure. Stuart plays a very different line here - simpler in places, but with some tasty fills in the second bar of the sequence - see bars 38 and 46 for examples.

The theme of this song is the concept of the 'Manifest Destiny', which was a phrase used to define the belief that white Americans had the right to occupy the entire North American continent. Other similar acts of large-scale colonisation - at the expense of another culture - are also said to be examples of Manifest Destiny.

Sadly, it would seem that this track has never been performed live by the band.

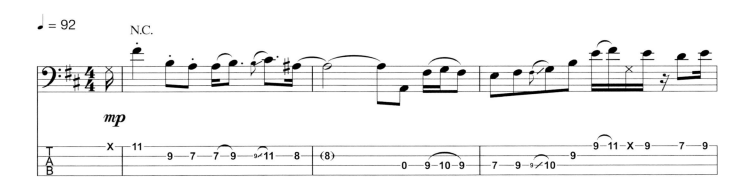

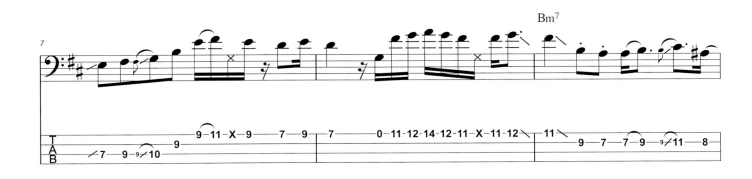

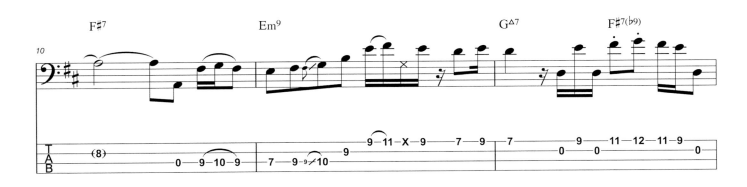

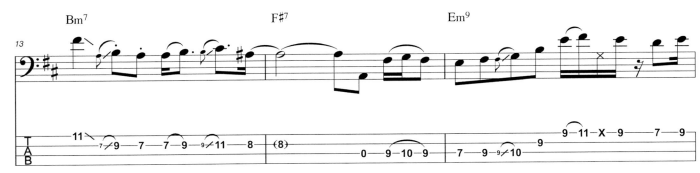

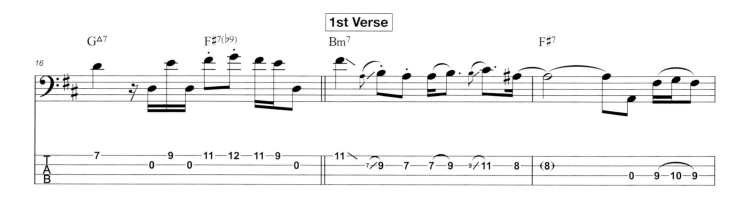

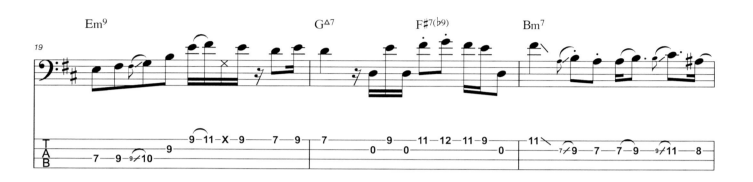

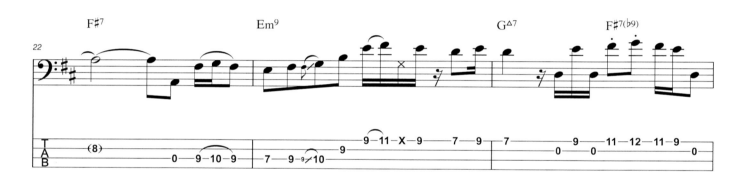

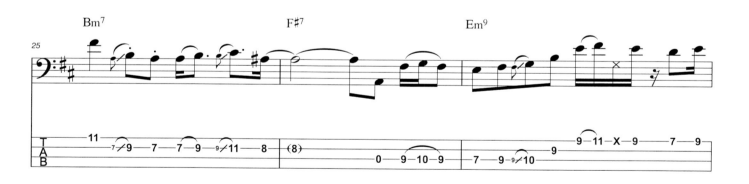

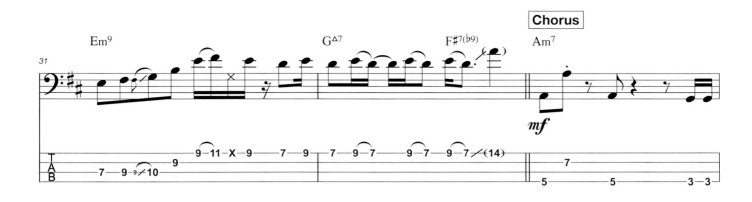

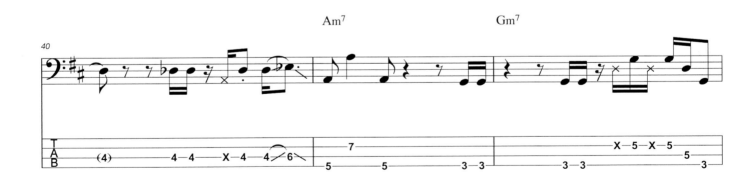

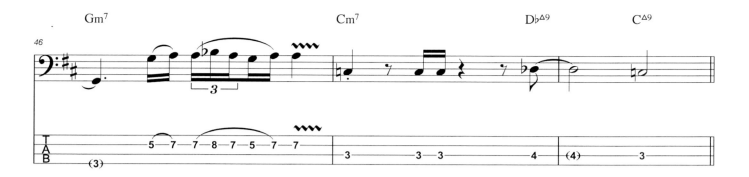

2nd Verse

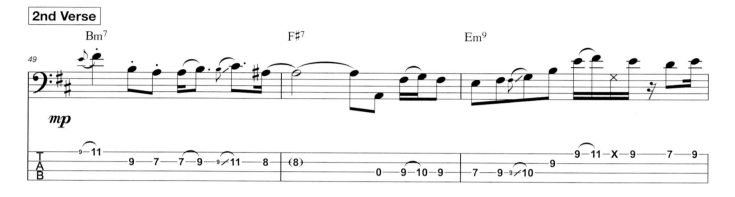

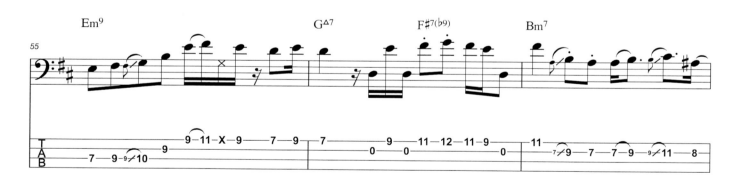

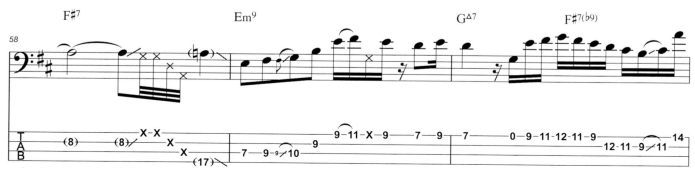

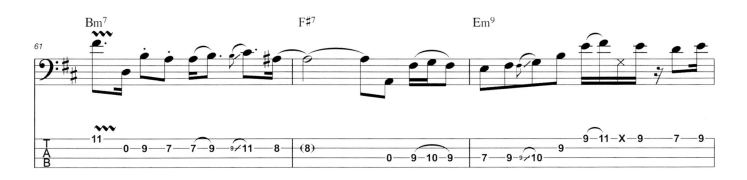

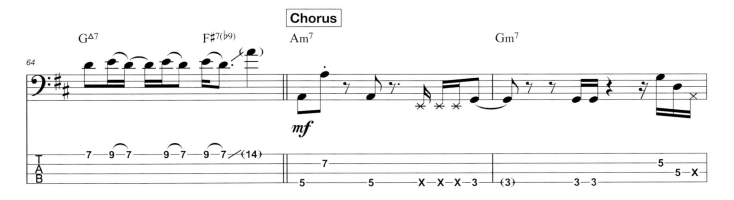

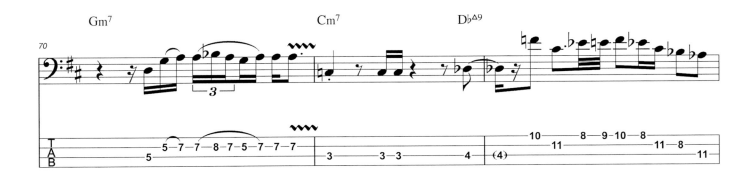

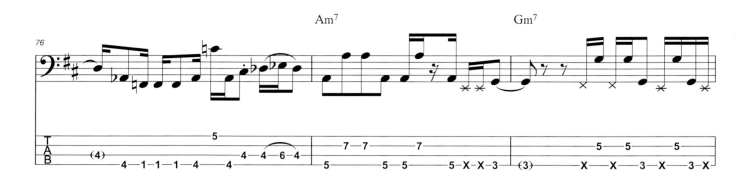

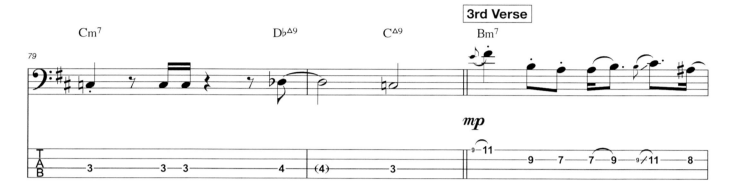

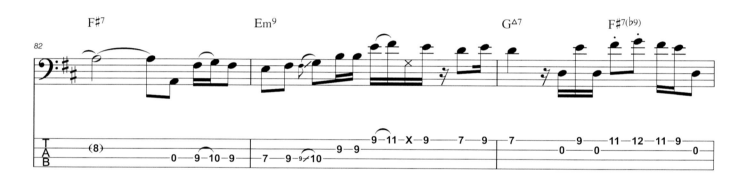

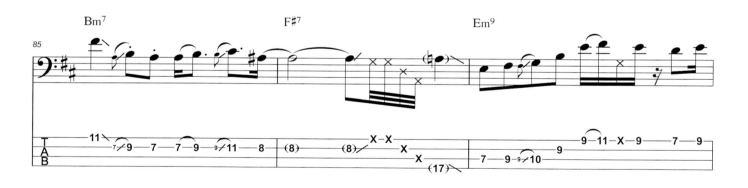

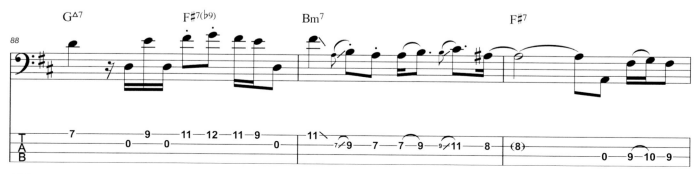

128

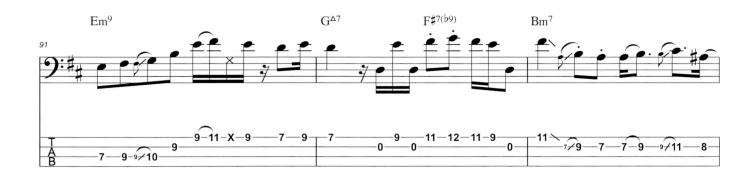

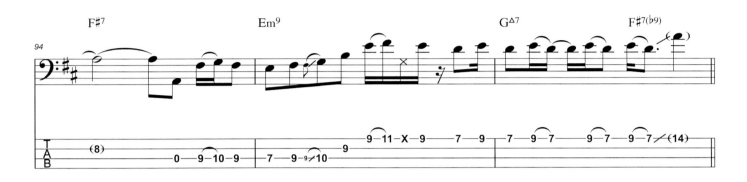

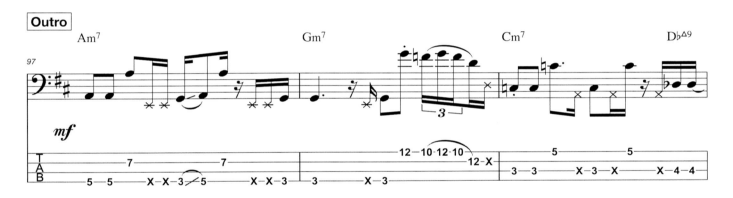

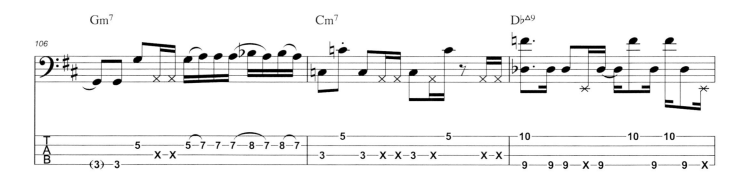

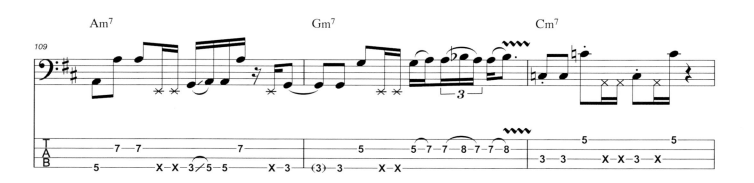

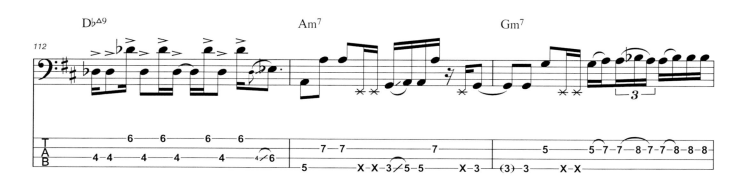

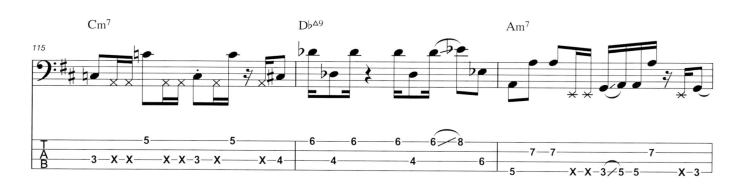

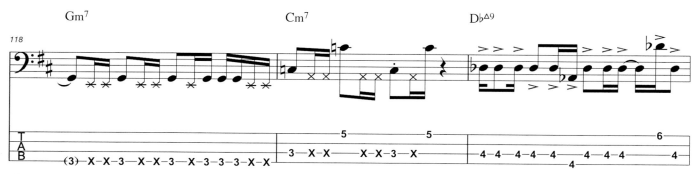

130

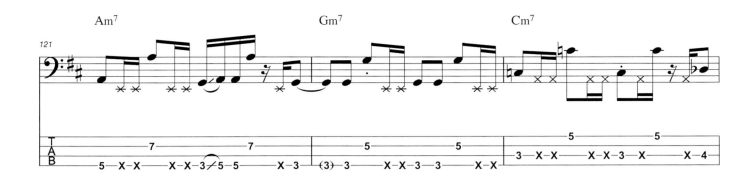

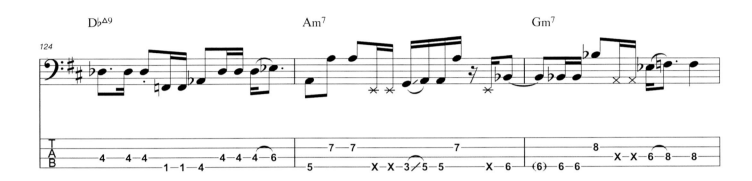

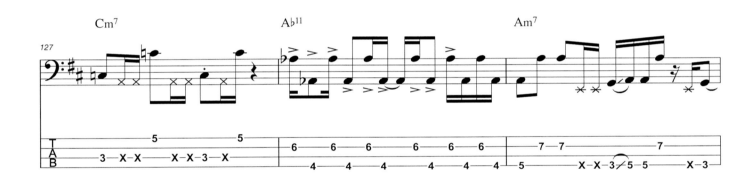

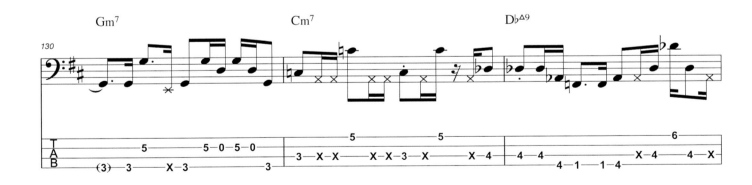

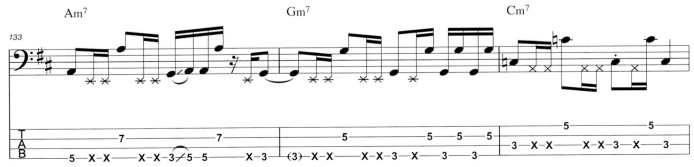

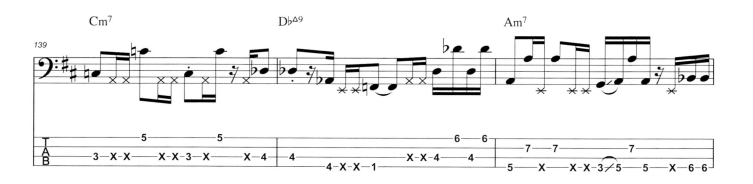

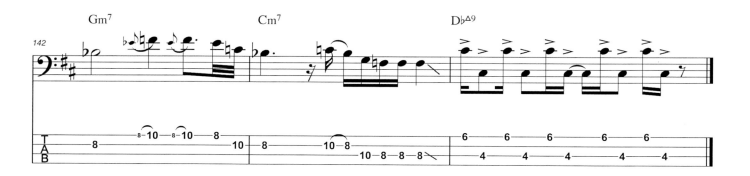

132

The Kids

Written By: Jason Kay/Toby Smith

'The Kids' is the most energetic track on *The Return of the Space Cowboy* and features yet more great bass work from the young Stuart Zender. This fast-paced funk workout is a nod to many of the band's seventies funk influences, and the heavily effected bass part certainly suggests a Bootsy Collins influence on Stuart.

The song opens with Toby Smith's heavily effected keyboard riff. After an opening note, the bass enters properly in bar 5 with a two-bar funk groove that is then used for the majority of the song. The bass uses effects here in order to mimic a synth-like tone - Stuart has reported using a Boss ME-8B live for this song, although the studio version sounds as though it could have been recorded with a Mutron pedal (an envelope filter) and a fuzz pedal. You can achieve similar results using an envelope filter and a fuzz - there are many varieties of each available.

The main two-bar groove that begins at bar 5 is based heavily on chord tones, implying chords of Gm^7, $B^\flat$ and C. Note that there are no actual chords played during this section, but the combination of the instrument parts suggests these chords. Stuart begins the line riffing between G and F before playing a part in the higher register. I recommend putting the first finger on the $B^\flat$ at the thirteenth fret of the A-string. This will allow you to comfortably play the $B^\flat$ again after the two F's. The ghost notes are important to the groove - it feels quite natural to play the first of these with the fretting hand (as you would use the left hand in the slap technique), and the second with the picking hand. The second bar of the sequence is heavily syncopated and implies a C^7 chord with the use of the $B^\flat$. Note that Stuart slides up to the $D^\flat$ briefly: the $D^\flat$ is the 'blue' note from the G minor pentatonic scale, which is an appropriate scale to use over this two-bar line. The final $B^\flat$ in the bar should have vibrato added to it. Stuart often uses 'shakes' in place of vibrato: if you wish to do the same, simply move your fretting hand finger rapidly between the $B^\flat$ and the B above - this is similar to a trill,

but is performed with one finger and has a slightly more 'fluid' sound. Shakes are a commonly used device in funk lines and they crop up often in Stuart Zender's playing.

The two-bar groove discussed above is used for the majority of the song, although there are some great variations to study. Check out the octave licks in bars 7 and 11, the alternative fill in bar 20 and the upper register licks in bars 41 and 49. These are similar to the part that was played in the opening section to 'Just Another Story', which was transcribed earlier in the book.

The bassline played during the Chorus is a typical funk line that sounds great with the effects. Be aware that staccato notes are particularly important during this section. You will also notice a staccato note with a slide away from it in bar 32: as soon as the note is played, slide quickly up the neck keeping the slide short and crisp. The Chorus section ends with a 2/4 unison bar.

During the Breakdown Stuart plays random ghost notes and slides. The actual pitches are not notated here as the slides are played for effect - they are more of a rhythmic device than a melodic one. This eight-bar section ends with a long glissando on the E-string which sounds great with the heavy use of the effects.

'The Kids' was a popular live track when the band toured in support of the album, and continues to be played live to this day. A great version from 2017 (with Paul Turner on bass) at the Moon and Stars Festival show in Locarno, Switzerland can be seen on YouTube.

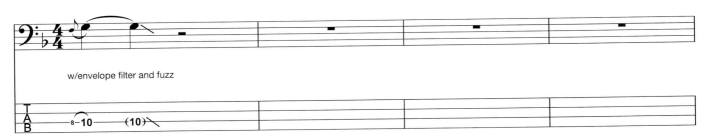

w/envelope filter and fuzz

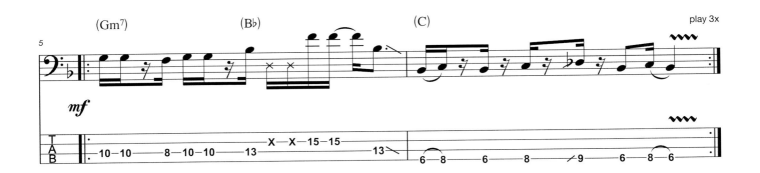

mf

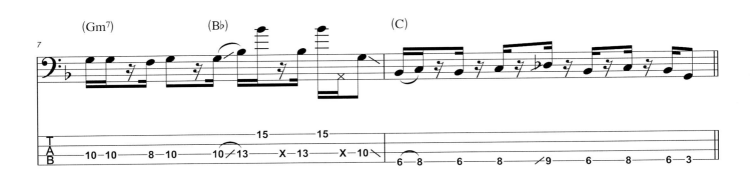

1st Verse

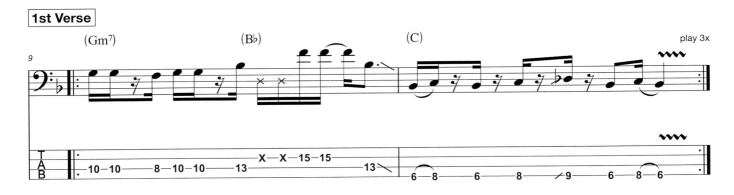

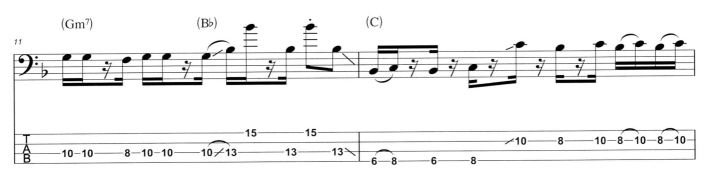

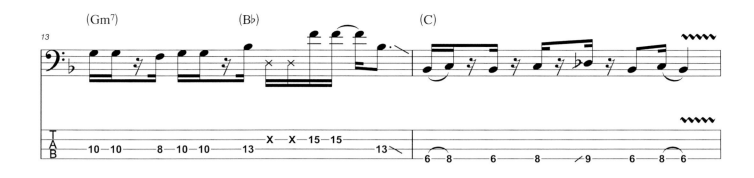

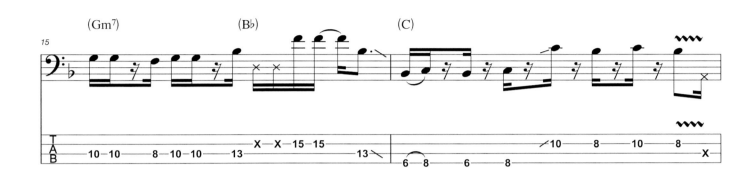

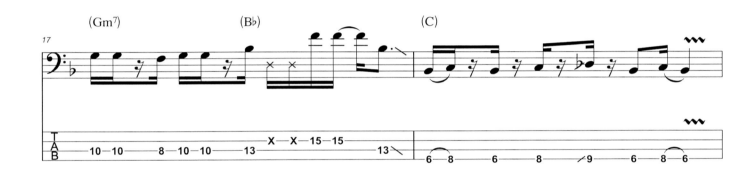

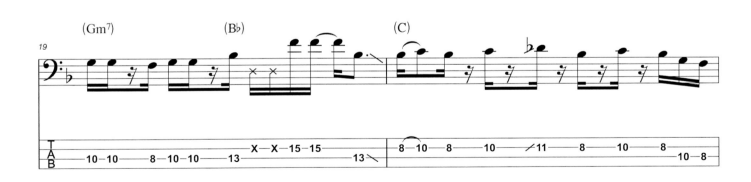

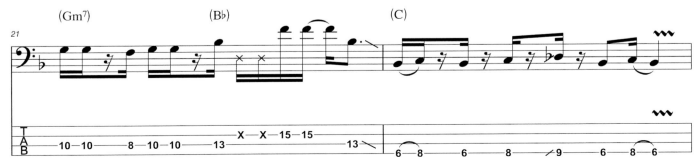

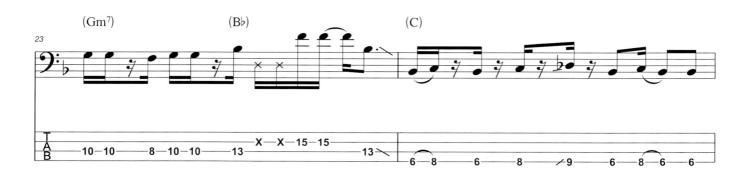

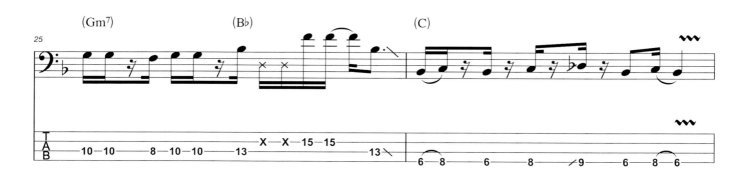

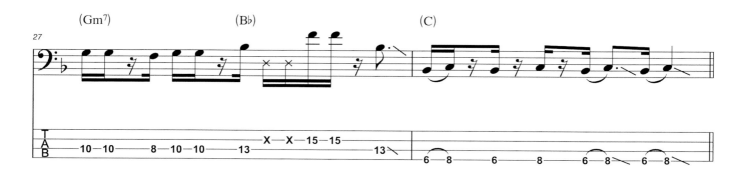

136

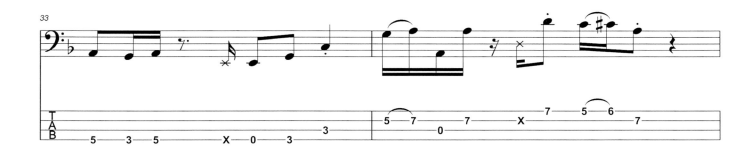

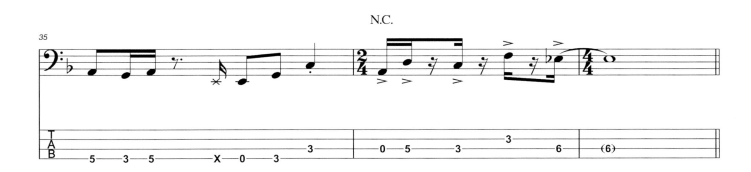

2nd Verse

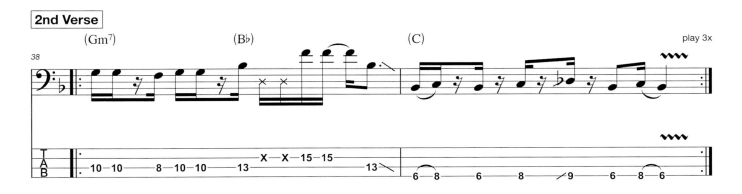

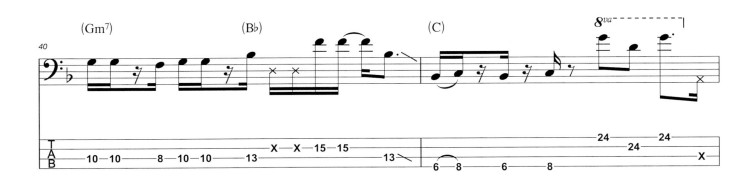

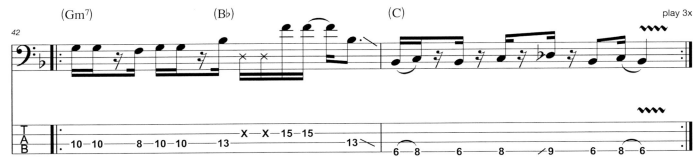

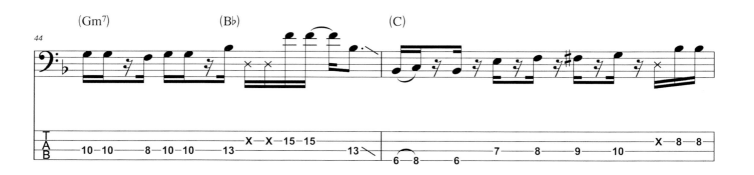

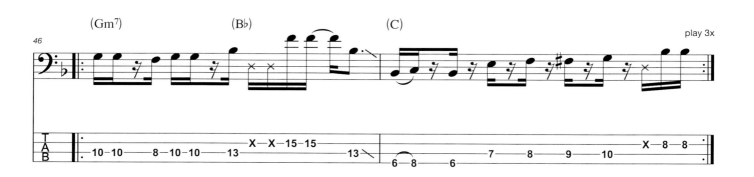

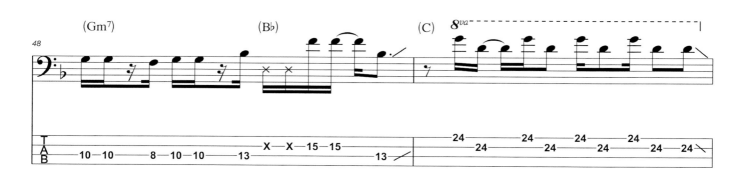

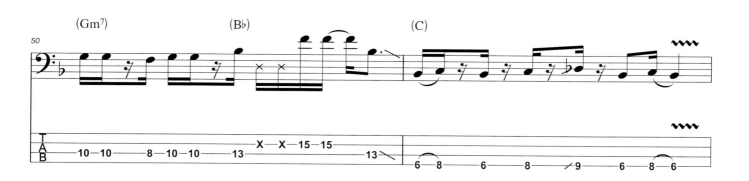

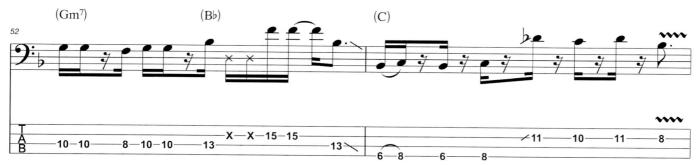

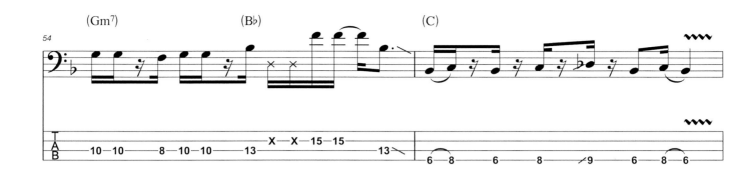

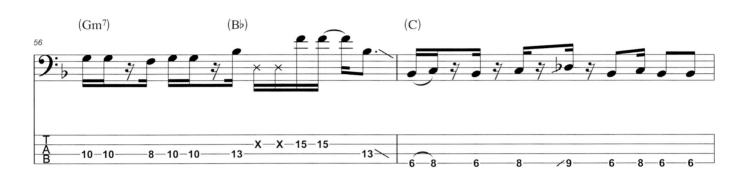

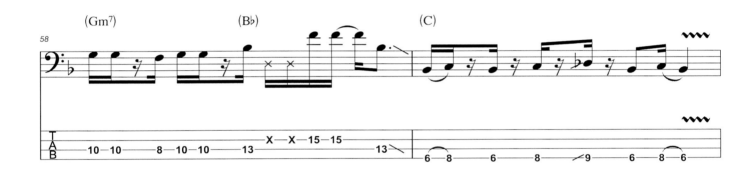

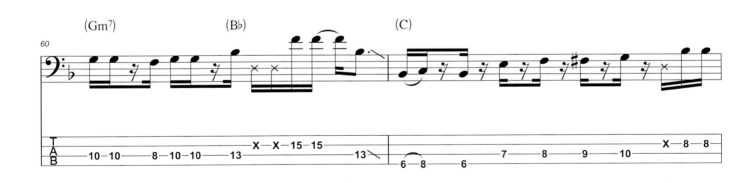

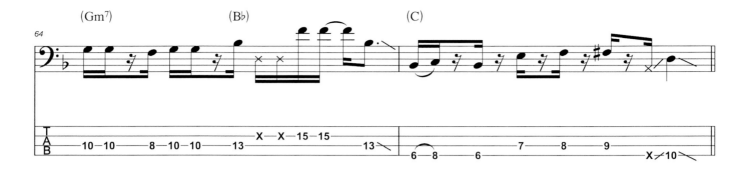

Chorus

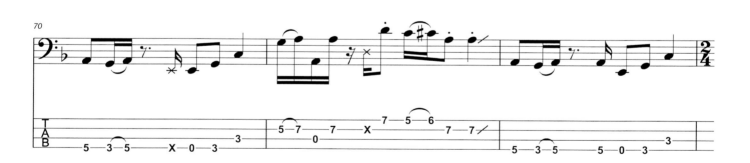

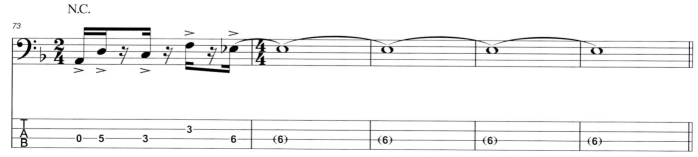

Breakdown

78

* all pitches approximate during Breakdown

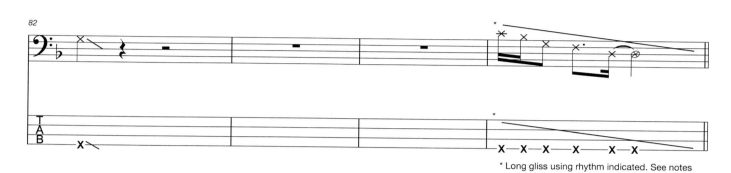

82

* Long gliss using rhythm indicated. See notes

Instrumental Section

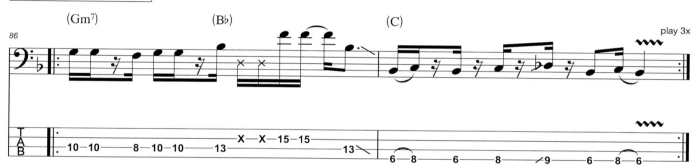

86

(Gm⁷) (B♭) (C) play 3x

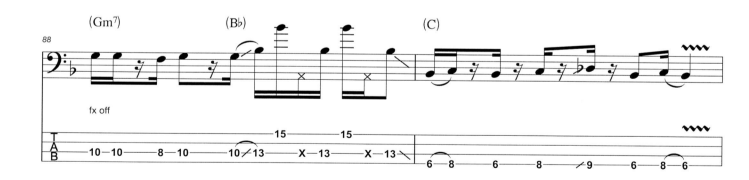

88

(Gm⁷) (B♭) (C)

fx off

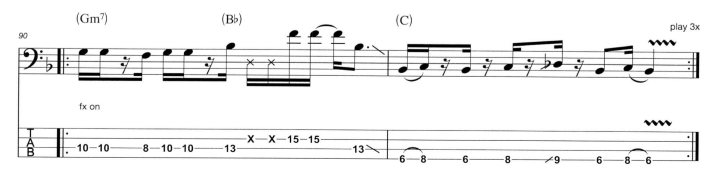

90

(Gm⁷) (B♭) (C) play 3x

fx on

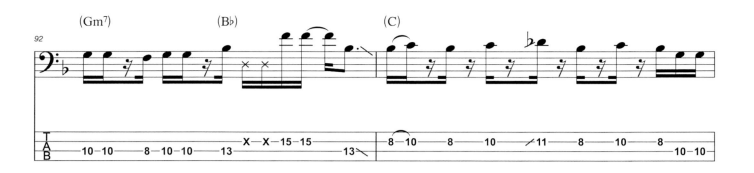

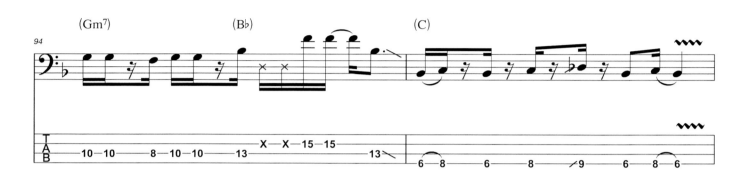

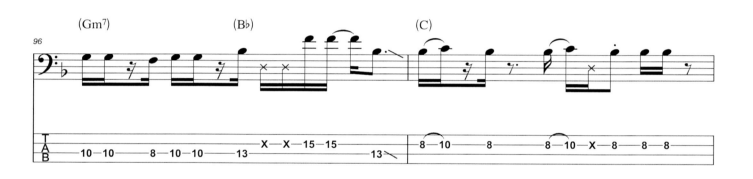

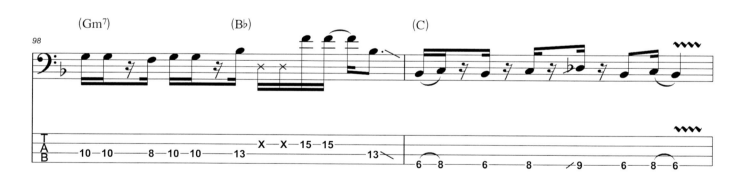

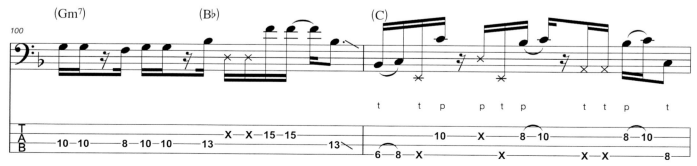

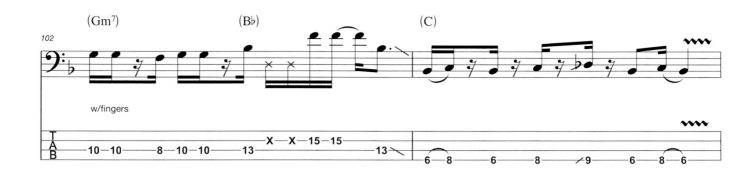

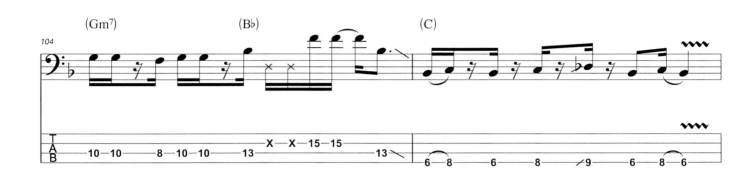

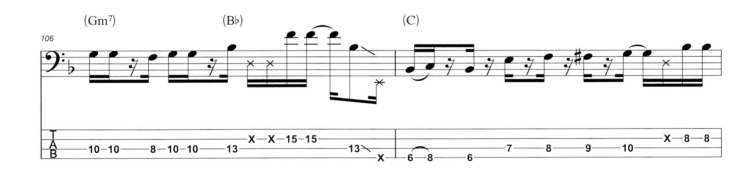

3rd Verse

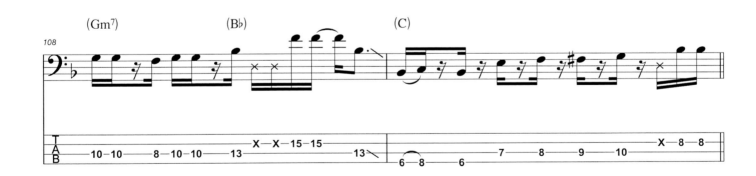

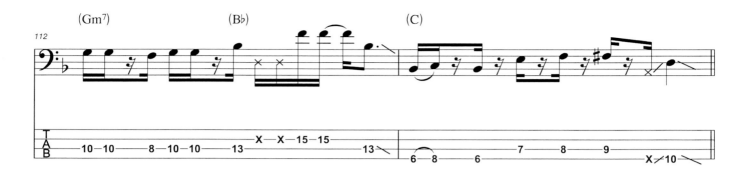

Chorus

(Am⁷)

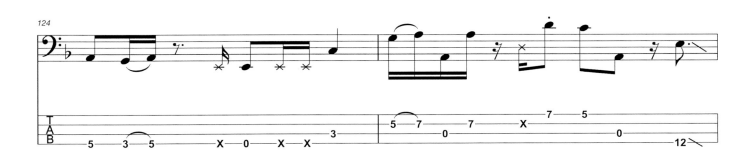

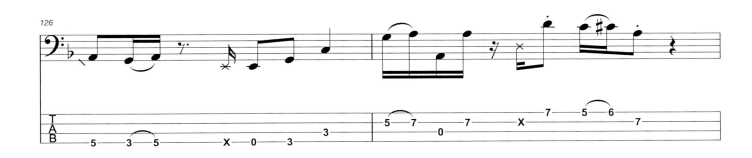

N.C.

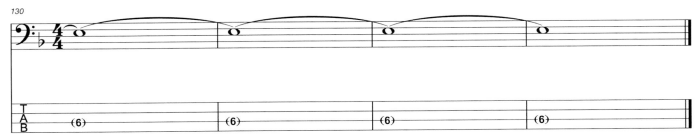

Mr. Moon

Written By: Jason Kay/Stuart Zender/Toby Smith

'Mr. Moon' features some fantastic playing from Stuart Zender and is one of his most popular grooves. This song is slapped throughout and is a real bass-feature, so it comes as no surprise that Stuart shares a writing credit on the track.

'Mr. Moon' opens with an eight-bar percussion/drums Intro after which Stuart sets up the four-bar bass groove that will underpin the Verse sections of the tune. When playing this groove, you should note the emphasis Stuart places on the second beat of each bar as well as his use of staccato notes. These are indicated in the notation, but not the TAB. This groove is used - with several variations on the basic theme - for many of the sections of the song.

The Chorus begins in bar 29 with a simple ascending chromatic line that follows the chord progression. The second bar of this repeating two-bar line has a semiquaver figure that has three D's in a row. Note that the first is hammered-on from the C, the second is slapped, and the third is played as an open D-string. After this, Stuart hits the minor third of the chord (F) and the seventh (C). This is followed by a B in most cases

with the remainder of the bar being different each time. Note Stuart's rapidly popped G's in bar 32 - these can be tough to articulate cleanly at this tempo. Stuart also plays a figure in bar 34 where he slides up to an approximate pitch of D (on the E-string) then pops the F on the G-string. The pitches in brackets are guides only - it does not matter which notes are struck as the hand slides upwards.

The two parts discussed so far are used throughout the remainder of the song, but as usual there are many variations to be studied along the way.

'Mr. Moon' is a popular live track, and was most recently played on the band's 2017 *Automaton* tour. A great version can be found on YouTube from the Moon and Stars Festival show in Locarno, Switzerland.

1st Verse

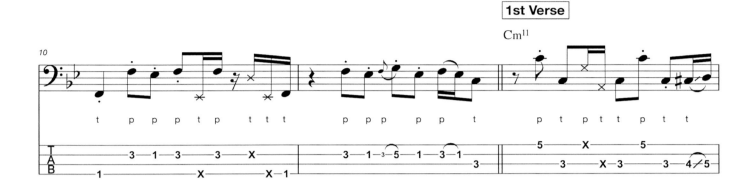

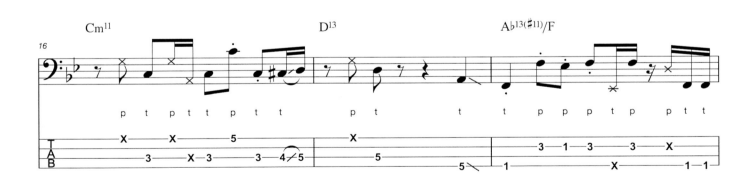

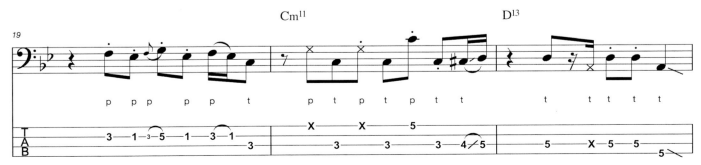

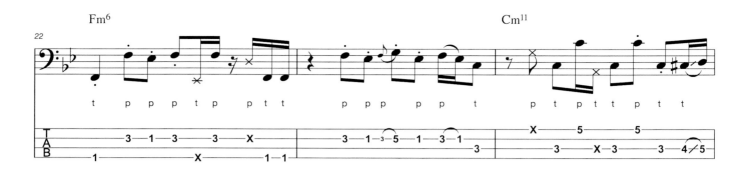

Chorus

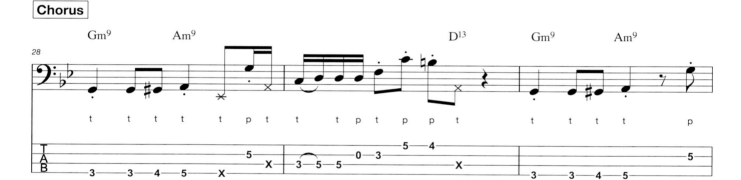

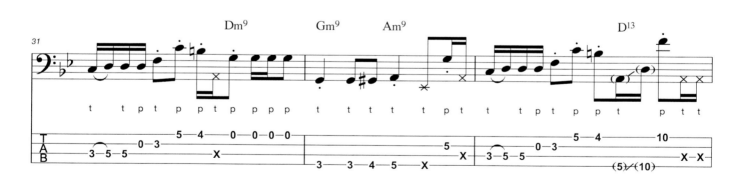

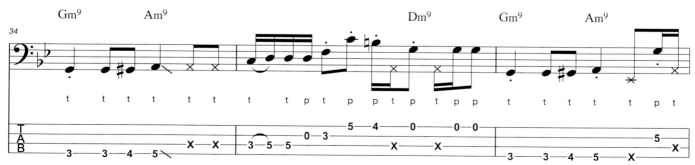

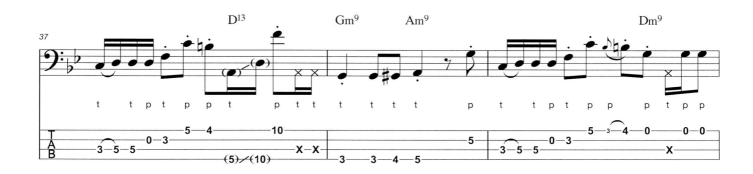

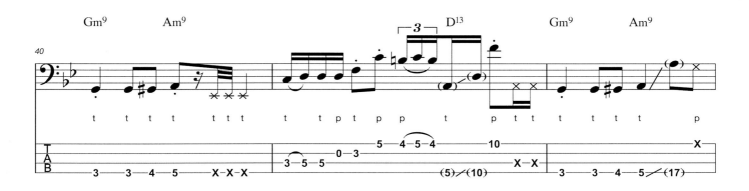

2nd Verse

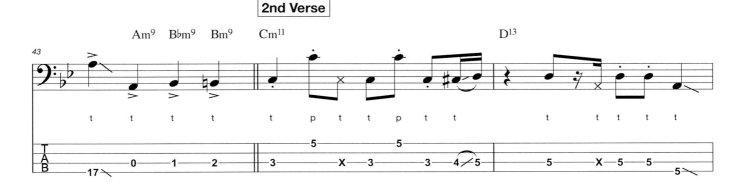

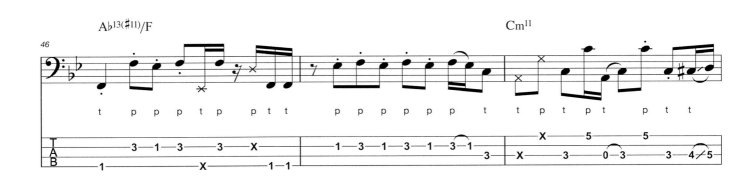

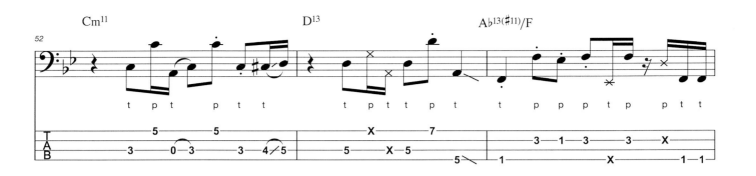

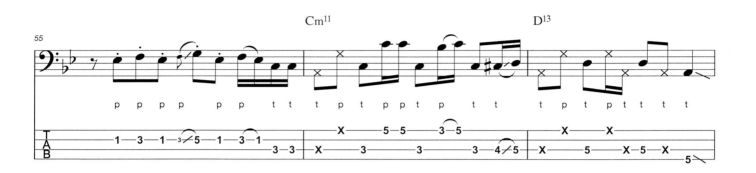

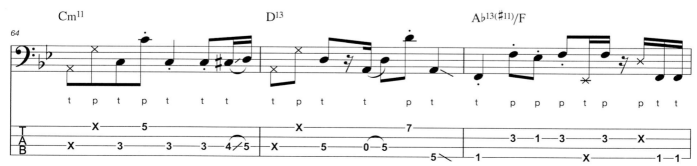

150

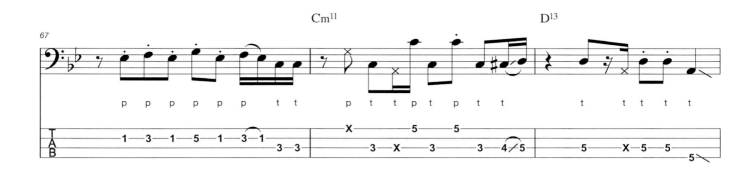

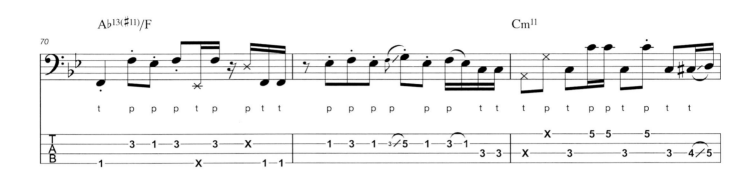

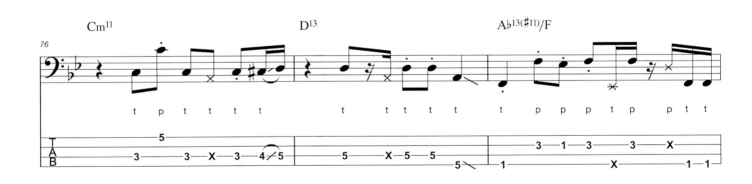

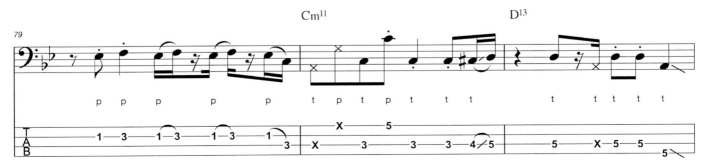

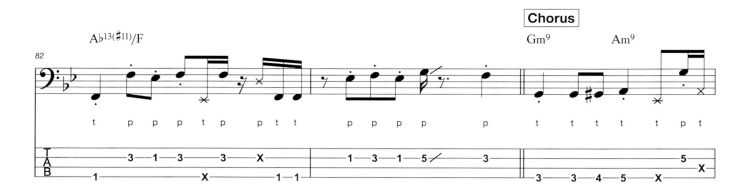

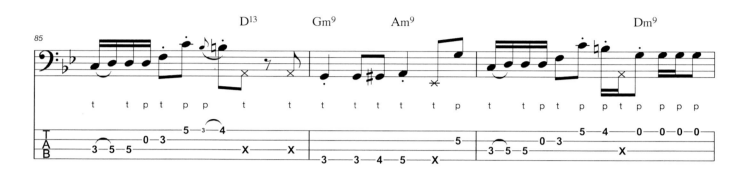

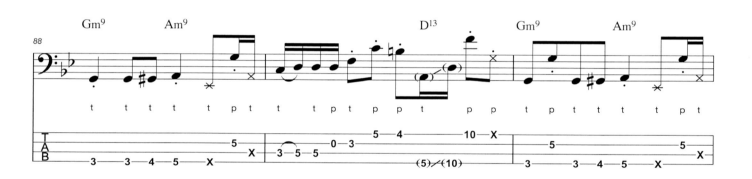

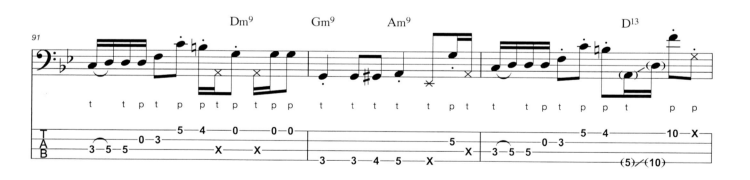

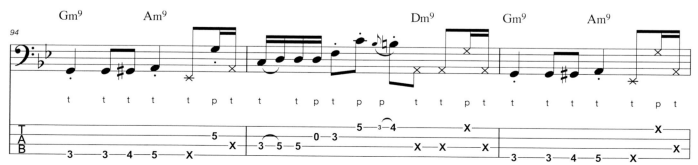

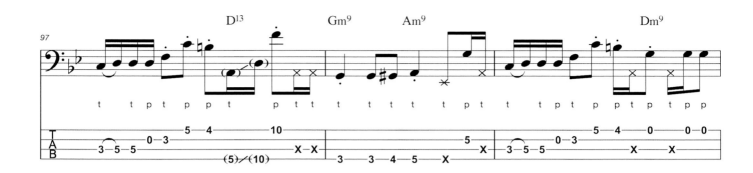

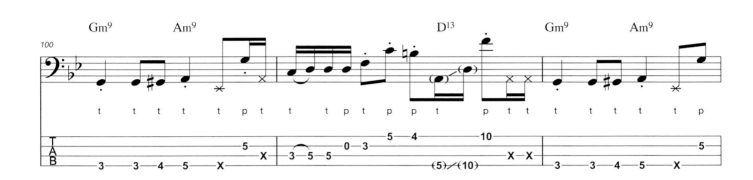

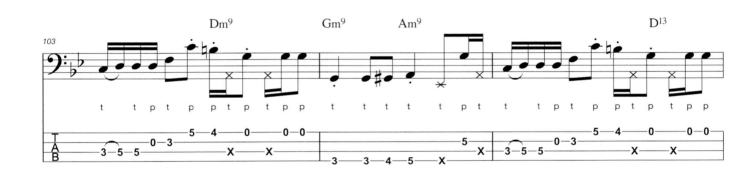

3rd Verse

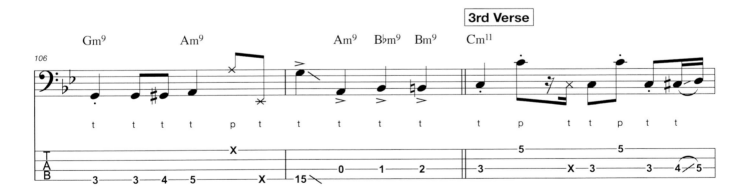

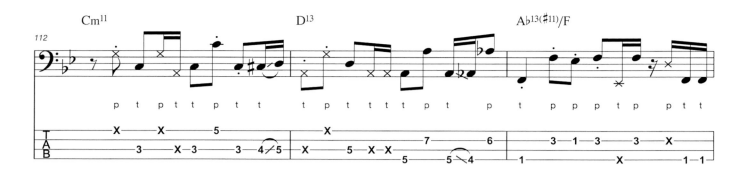

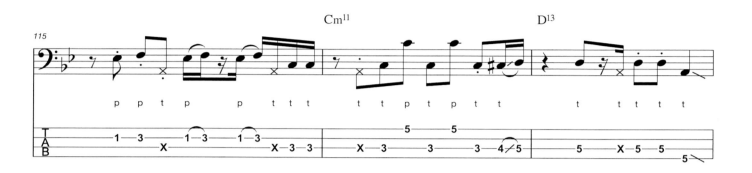

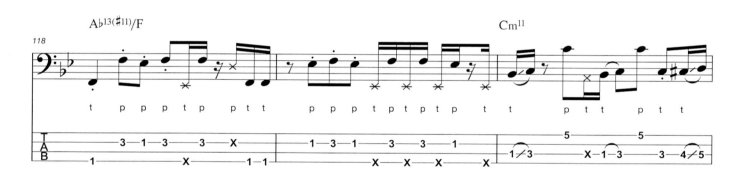

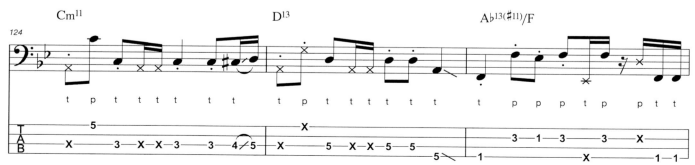

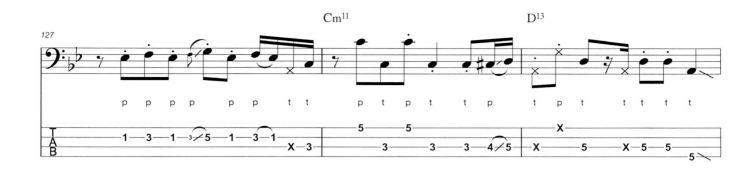

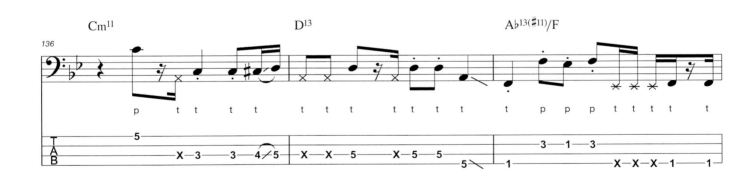

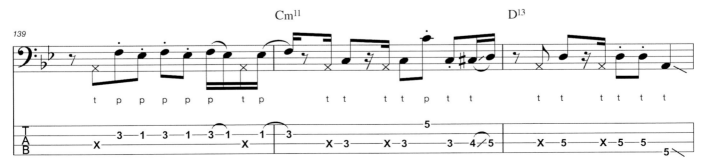

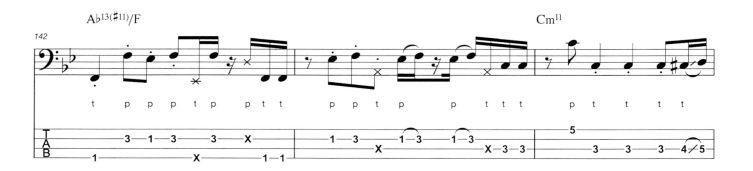

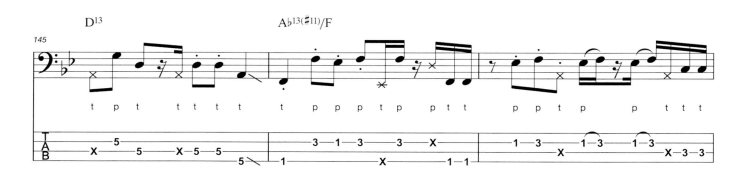

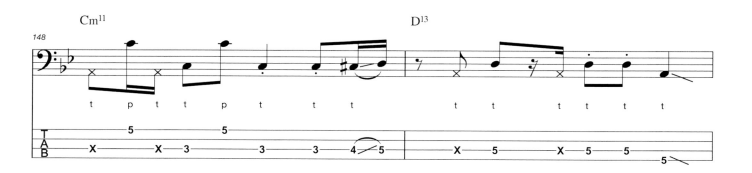

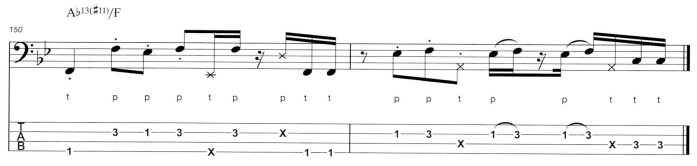

Fade Out

Scam

Written By: Jason Kay/Stuart Zender

'Scam' features one of the most popular bass grooves from the *Return of the Space Cowboy* album and is undoubtedly one of Stuart Zender's finest recorded lines. The song is predominantly based around two heavy slap grooves, but the Outro section also features some nimble fingerstyle work.

The track opens with an ascending figure that builds in volume over the course of the next eight bars – Stuart plays a simple root note line here. This is followed by a continuation of this part, but the bassline becomes a more active slap and pop line at this point.

The main groove of the song enters in bar 18. This is a two-bar line based around an ascending F - F♯- G slap and pop figure in the first bar, followed by a fingerstyle phrase in the second. Each of the ascending notes is preceded by an open E-string and hammer-on, giving the line a driving semiquaver feel. Open strings are also crucial to the fingerstyle part of the line, so be sure to play these exactly as indicated in the TAB. There are many variations on this line throughout the song, the most notable of which is found in bar 25, and is used sporadically throughout the track. Here, Zender starts his phrase on a popped B♭ at the third fret of the G-string and allows this to ring whilst he slaps the ascending figure below. This creates a chordal effect which reinforces the underlying Gm^7 chord. A similar idea is used in bar 29, although this time with octaves of the ascending line.

During the Chorus (beginning in bar 57) Stuart plays a different line, and it is one that features some tricky syncopations. This part is also based on an ascending F - F♯- G figure, this time an octave higher. Note placings - particularly the F at the end of the first bar of the phrase - can be tricky to nail accurately, so you should work on this line at a slow tempo in order to achieve the results you hear on the record. This part also features some upper register 'shakes' which are a classic funk bass move, and a common feature in Stuart's playing.

Over the course of the song there is a large amount of repetition. However, the line has been transcribed in full as there are plenty of subtle variations that are well worth studying.

The songs transitions into an Outro section at bar 135 with a repeating four-bar line that is mostly played with the fingerstyle technique. This is a simple line, but the key to playing it well lies in the dynamics: staccato markings and volume indications should be followed carefully here. Bar 144 also contains a great fill for you to check out.

'Scam' was the result of combining two songs from the *Emergency on Planet Earth* era that were only ever played live. These were 'Do That Dance' and 'Life Goes On' - both can be found on YouTube. It was played live regularly during the band's early years and a great live performance can be heard on the band's performance at the Montreux Jazz Festival in 1995 (available to see on YouTube).

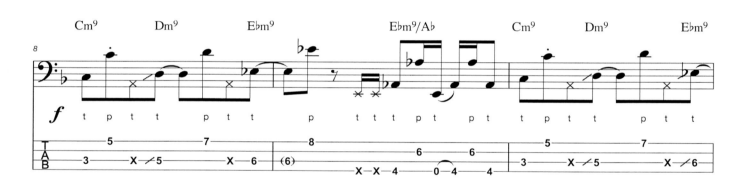

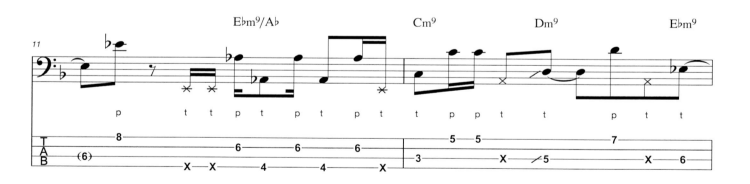

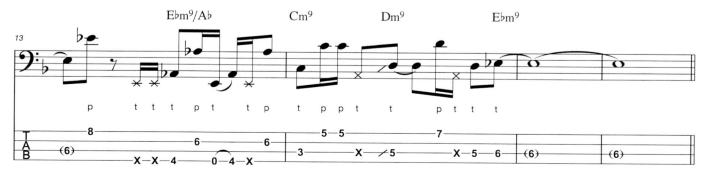

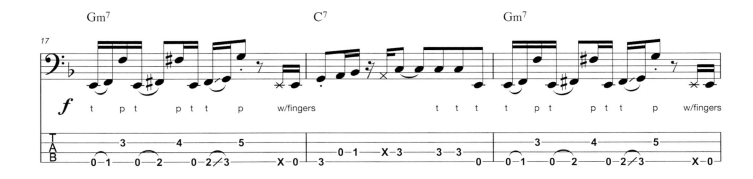

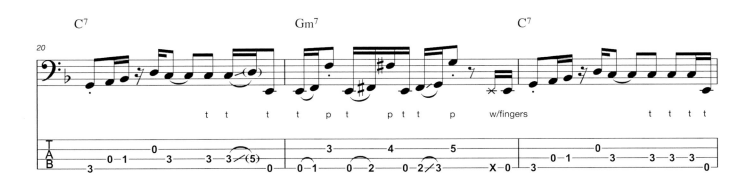

1st Verse

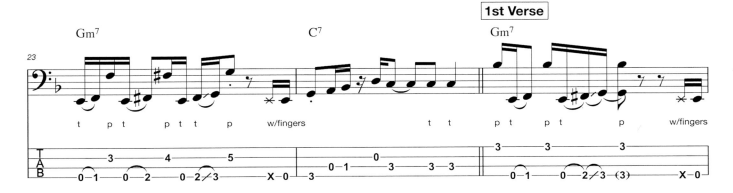

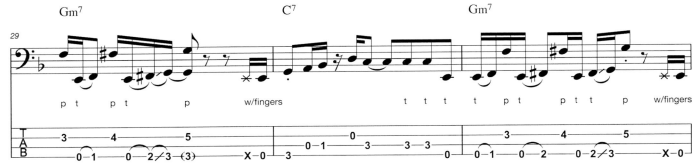

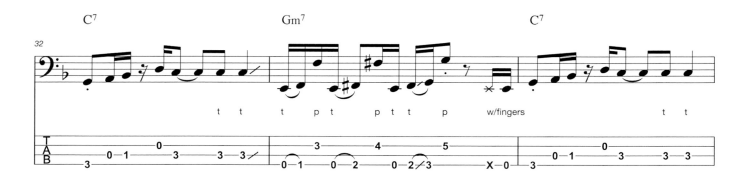

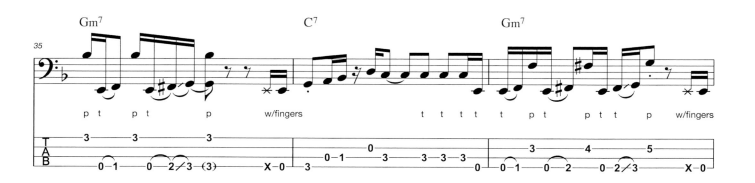

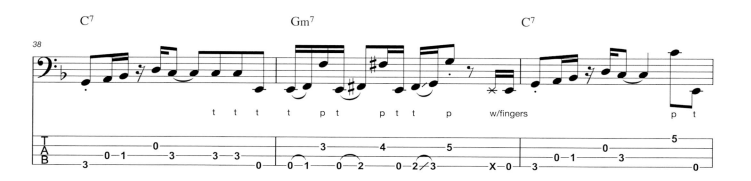

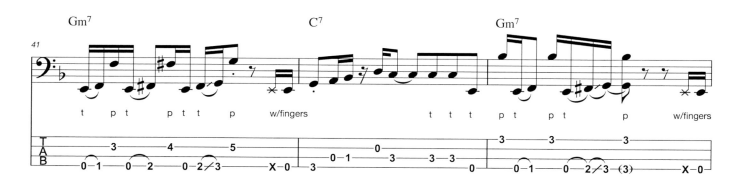

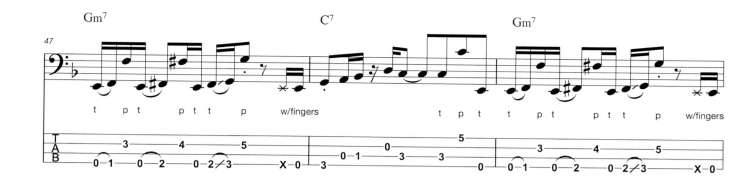

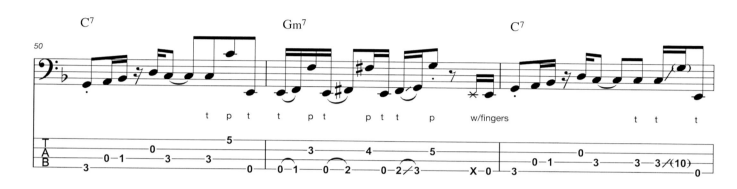

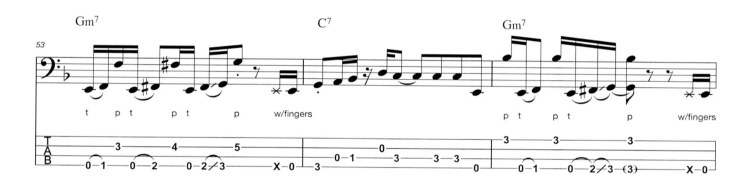

Chorus

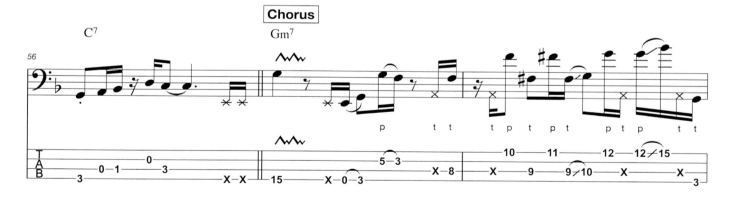

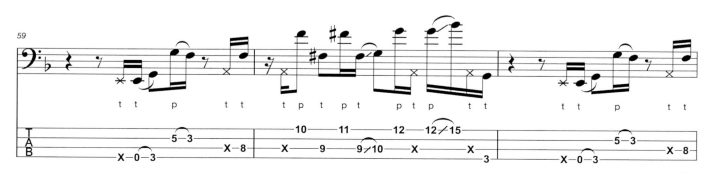

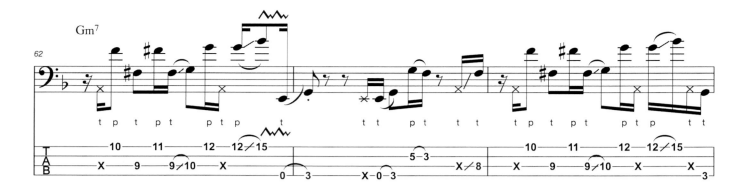

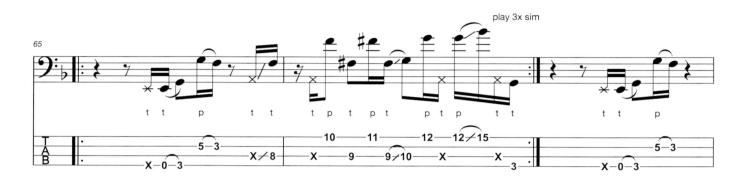

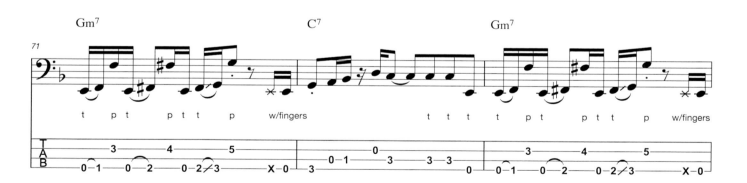

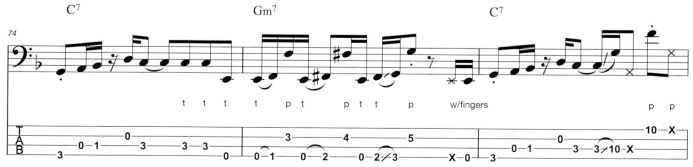

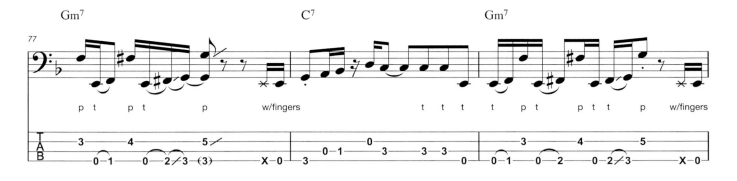

2nd Verse

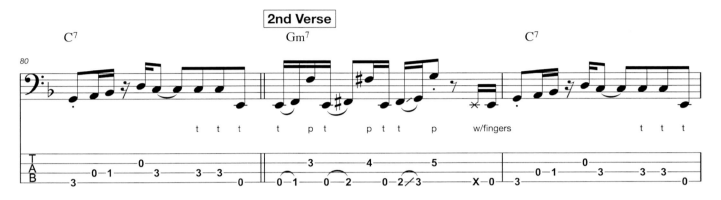

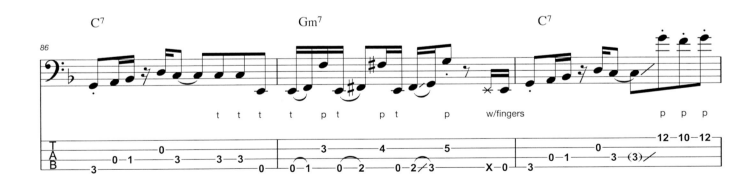

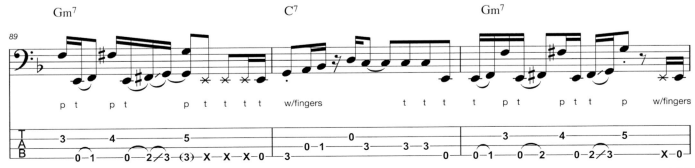

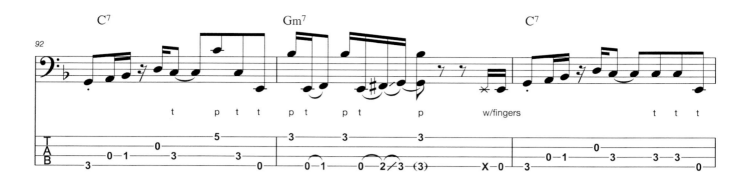

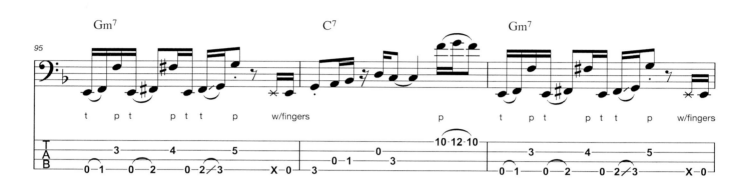

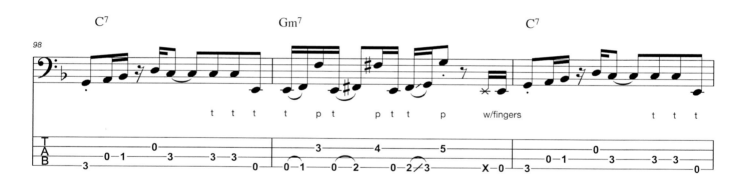

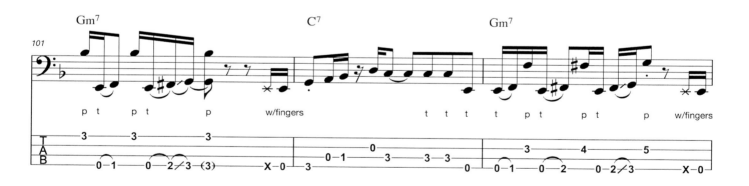

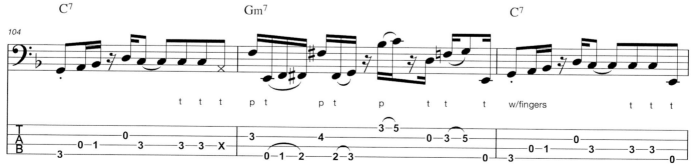

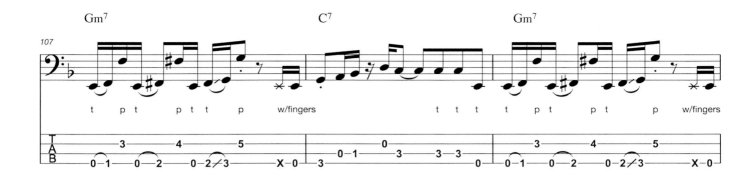

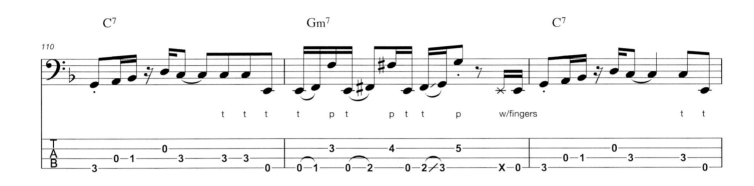

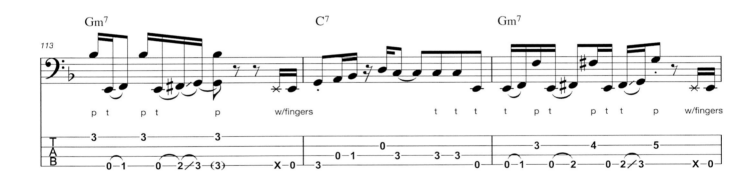

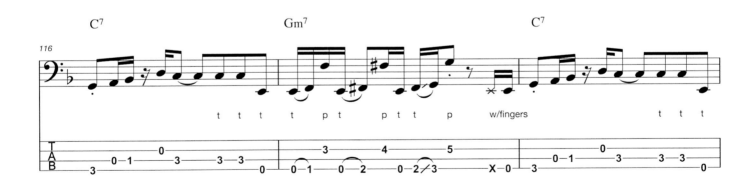

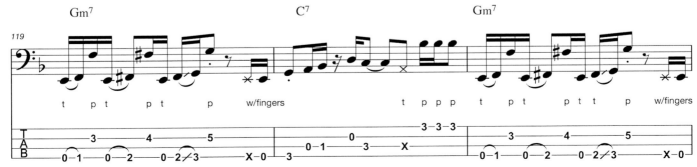

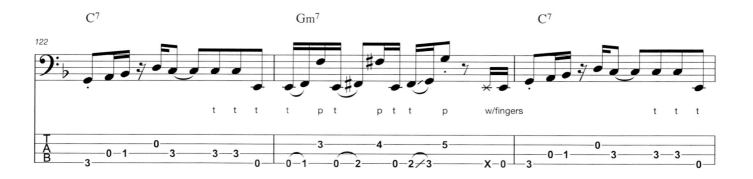

Chorus

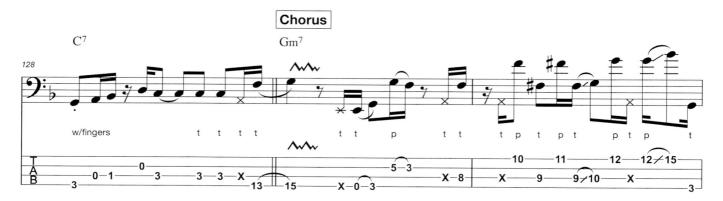

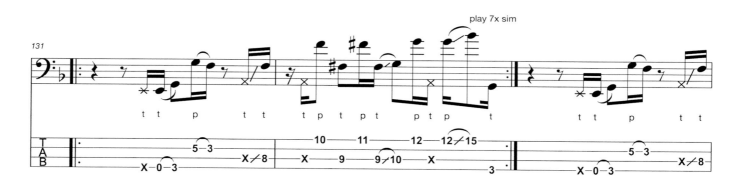

Outro

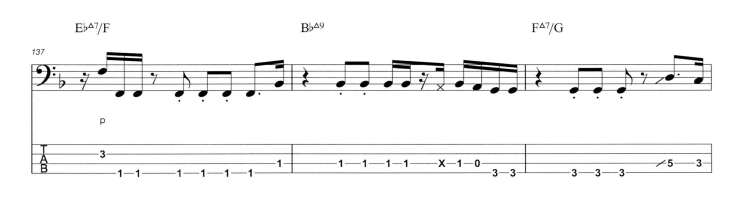

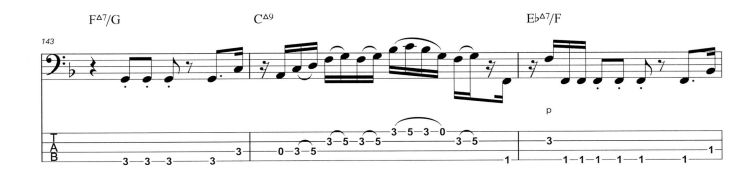

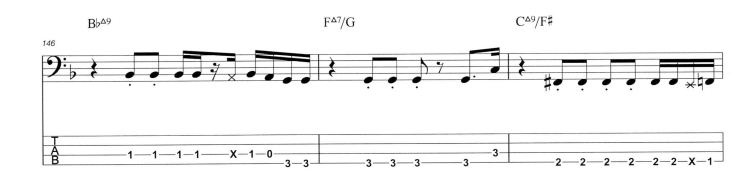

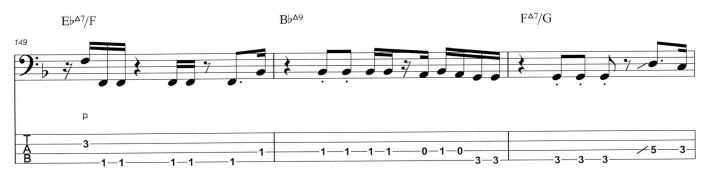

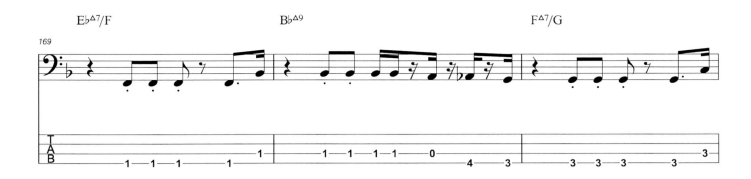

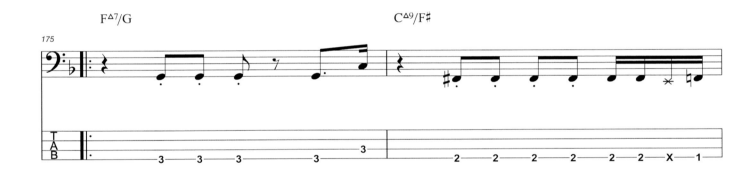

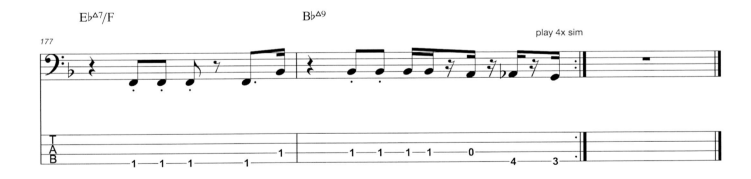

Space Cowboy

Written By: Jason Kay

'Space Cowboy' was the first single to be released from the *Return of the Space Cowboy* album and reached #17 in the UK, spending five weeks on the chart altogether. It was also a success in the U.S., reaching #1 on the Dance Chart. There are two versions of this song: the album version, and another version known as the 'Stoned Again Mix'. The latter is actually the original and is the version that is played live. The album version (transcribed here) was recorded while bassist Stuart Zender was absent from the studio, requiring Jay Kay to hire another bass player to record the part heard on the album. This bass player is referred to in the album liner notes as 'Mr. X' and has never been identified.

The song opens with two bars of Toby Smith's Rhodes piano before the band enters in bar 3. The bass part during the first verse is sparse, with the un-named player sticking mainly to roots, fifths and octaves for each chord, with occasional chromatic passing figures used to add interest. From the beginning, it is clear that the bassline is largely improvised, with no real 'hook' until the line in bar 14 that is used to move into the Chorus.

The Chorus is a repeating two-bar figure, and the bassline at this point closely follows the syncopated chord movement in the first bar, with the second bar of the sequence providing opportunities for fills. Most of the fills played in this first Chorus are based around the chord tones of the B$\flat$m^9 chord - B$\flat$ D$\flat$, F, A$\flat$ and C. The Chorus is followed by an Interlude section during which the bass plays a heavily syncopated chromatic figure. This brief funk workout provides a nice contrast to the rest of the tune.

The line gradually gets busier throughout the second Verse and Chorus and there are some tasty sixteenth note-based fills that are worthy of your attention during these sections. Check out bars 51, 55, and 65 for some great examples. The second Chorus is followed by another Interlude section with another great fill in bars 78-79 - note the use of the blues scale here.

The song now moves through several repeats of the Chorus, anchored by a fantastic bassline which is stuffed full of great fills, while also making excellent use of the lower notes offered by the 5-string bass. At bar 123 the track winds down into a quieter section. The notes in bars 138 and 139 are played with the palm muting technique - simply rest the palm of the right hand against the strings in order to deaden them as heard on the record. This section builds back up into a final Chorus beginning in bar 147.

You should be sure to also check out Stuart Zender's line on the 'Stoned Again Mix'. Comparing the two different bassist's approaches to this tune will help you get even more out of learning it.

This song is one of the band's most popular pieces and has been a regular fixture on the set-list for many years. It was most recently played on their 2017 *Automaton* tour.

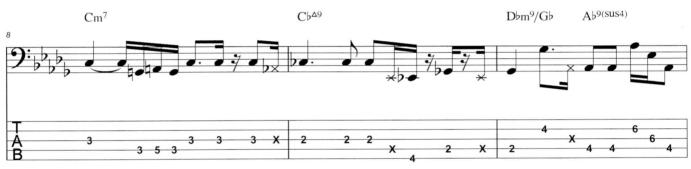

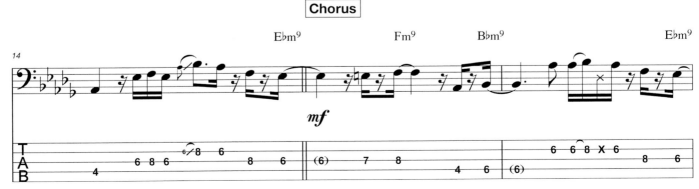

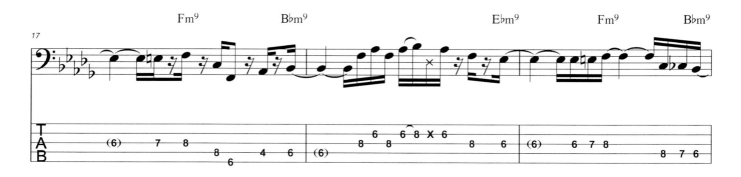

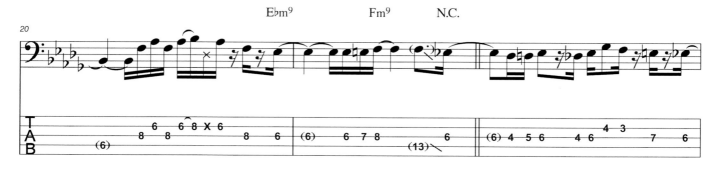

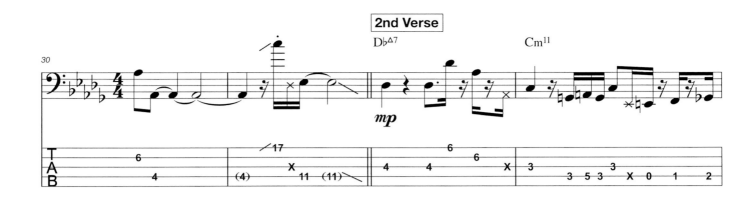

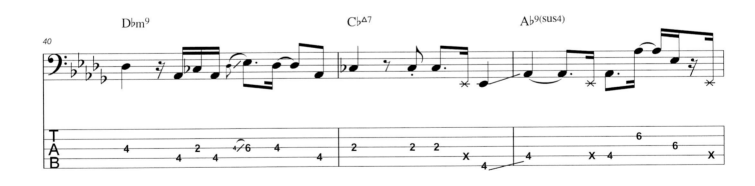

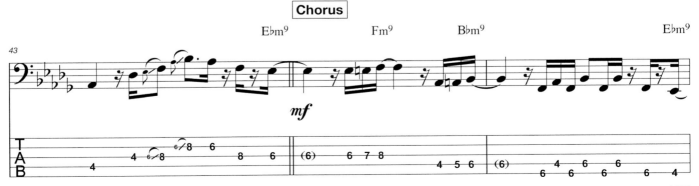

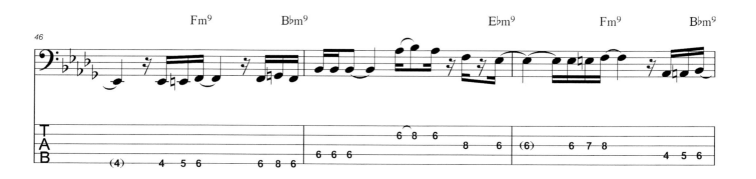

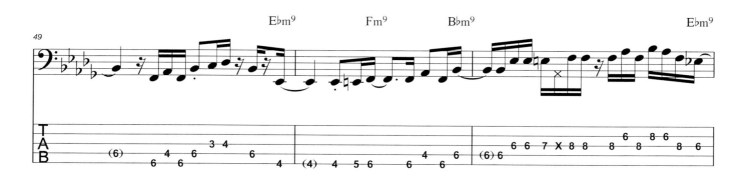

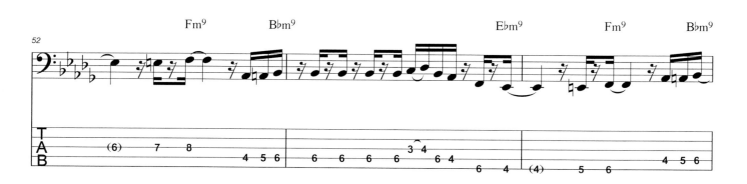

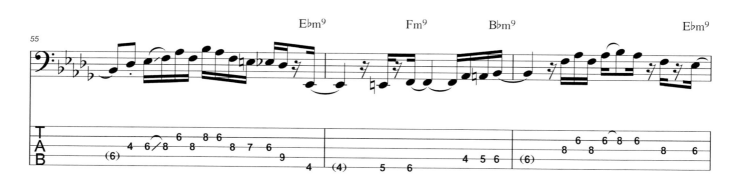

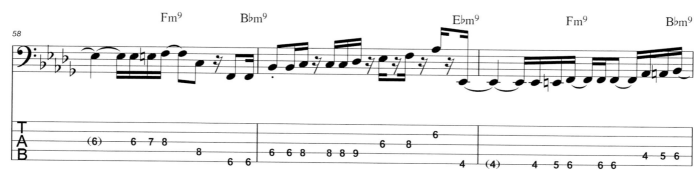

174

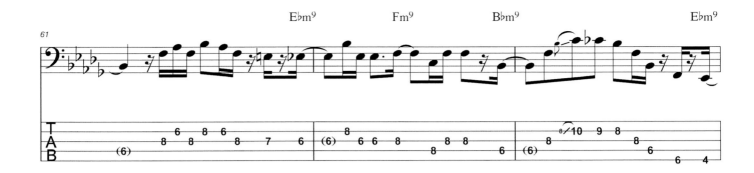

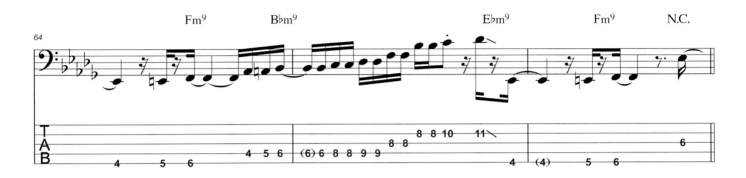

Interlude

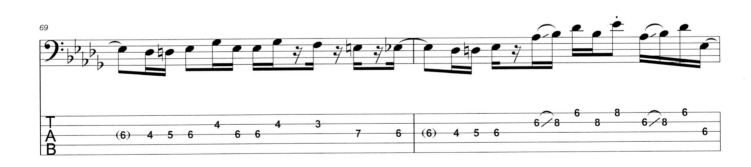

Chorus

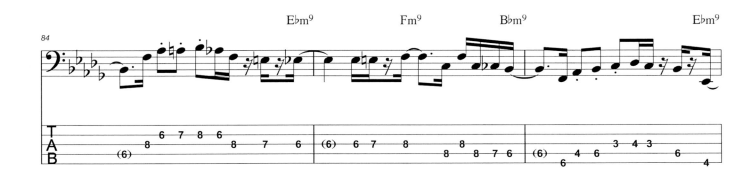

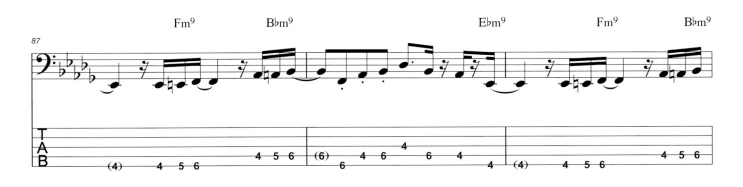

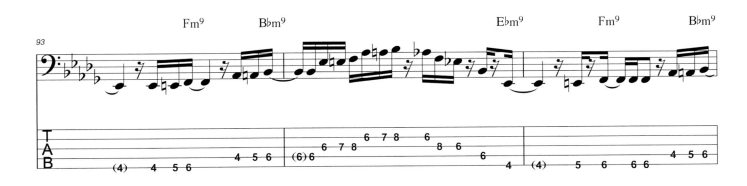

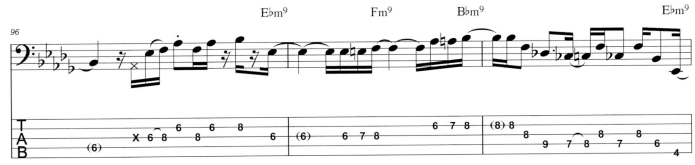

177

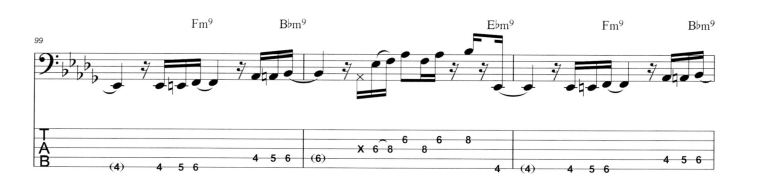

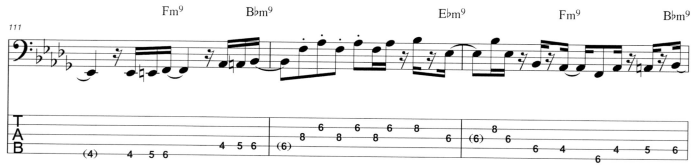

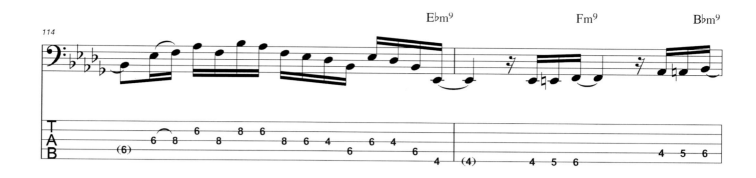

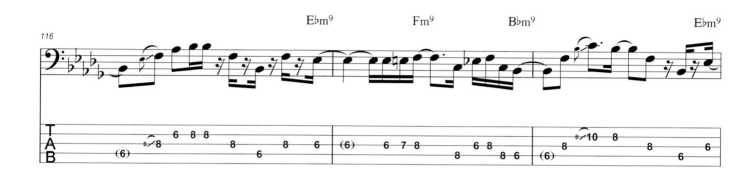

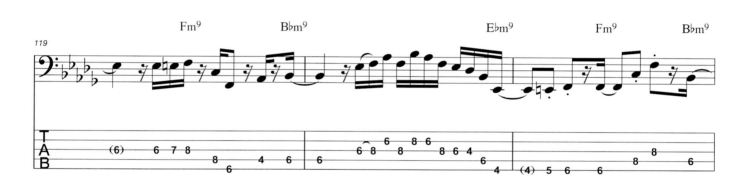

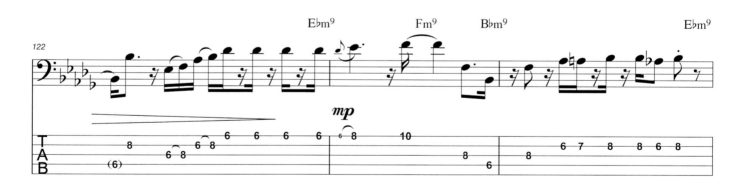

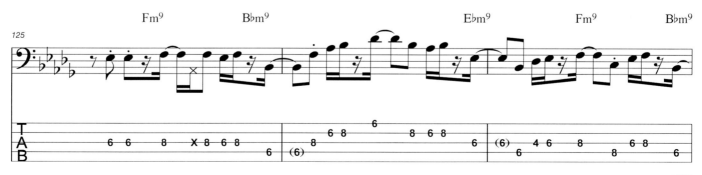

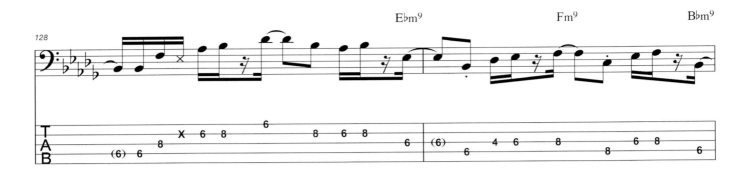

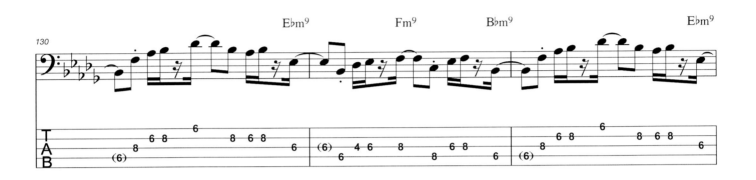

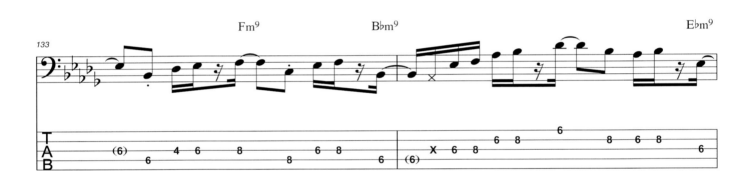

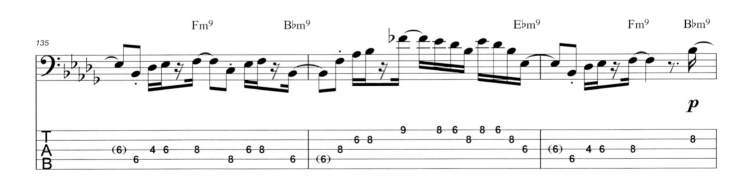

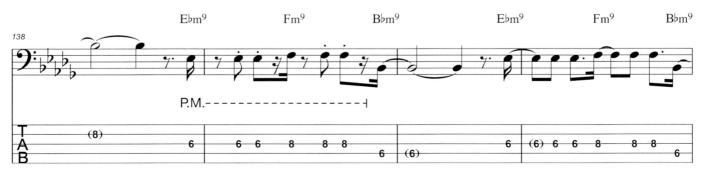

Chorus

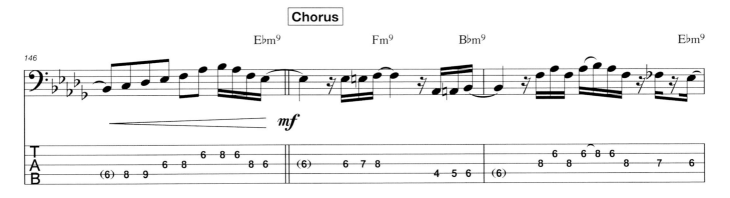

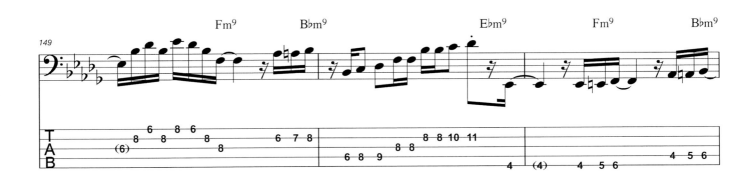

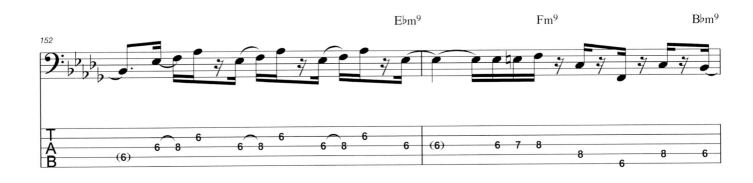

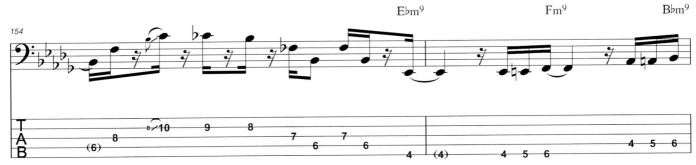

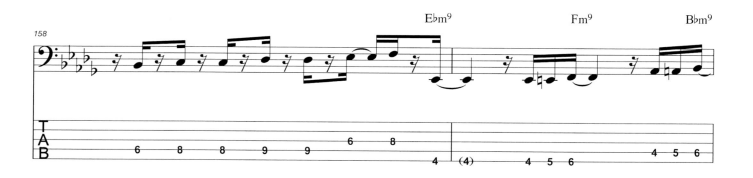

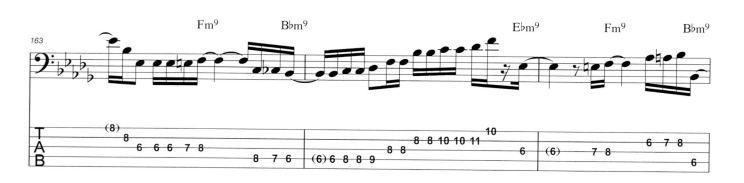

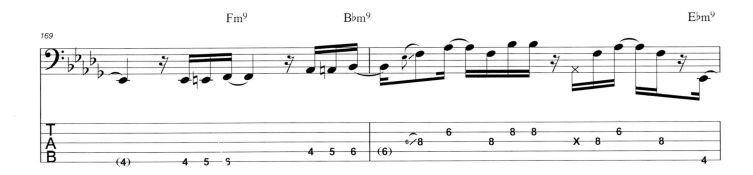

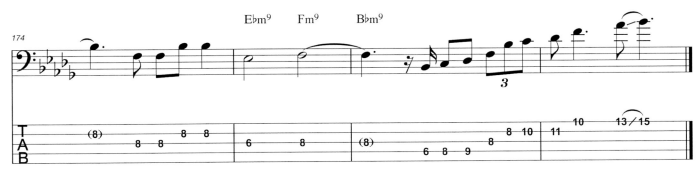